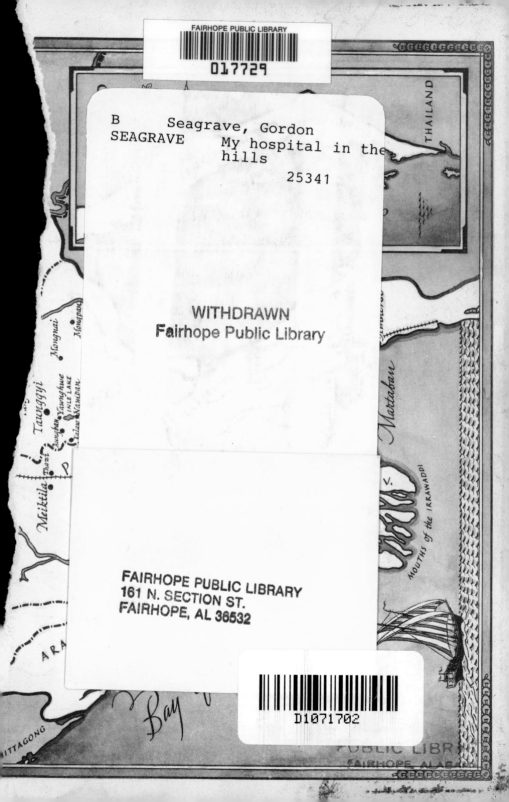

MY HOSPITAL IN THE HILLS

Other books by Gordon S. Seagrave

BURMA SURGEON
BURMA SURGEON RETURNS

MY
HOSPITAL
IN THE
HILLS

GORDON S. SEAGRAVE, M.D.

W · W · NORTON & COMPANY · INC ·

NEW YORK

TO
MY SISTER
GRACE RUSSELL SEAGRAVE, M.D.,
and to
THE PEOPLE OF BURMA
FOR WHOM SHE DIED

Contents

Illustrations

9

MY HOSPITAL IN THE HILLS

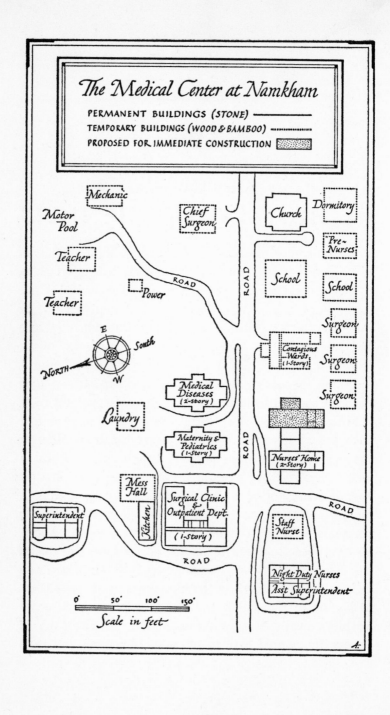

The Medical Center at Namkham

PERMANENT BUILDINGS (STONE) ————
TEMPORARY BUILDINGS (WOOD & BAMBOO) ·············
PROPOSED FOR IMMEDIATE CONSTRUCTION ▒▒▒▒

Mechanic

Motor Pool

Teacher

Teacher

Power

Chief Surgeon

ROAD

ROAD

Church

Dormitory

Pre-Nurses

School

School

Surgeon

Contagious Wards (1-story)

Surgeon

Surgeon

Medical Diseases (2-story)

Laundry

Maternity & Pediatrics (1-story)

Nurses' Home (2-story)

Mess Hall

Kitchen

Superintendent

Surgical Clinic & Outpatient Dept.

(1-story)

ROAD

Staff Nurse

ROAD

Night Duty Nurses

Ass't Superintendent

0'   50'   100'   150'

Scale in feet

A.

Publisher's Foreword

IN THE remote wilds of Northeast Burma, long before a world war threatened, Dr. Gordon Seagrave was carrying on his own war against misery, disease and death as a missionary doctor in the little village of Namkham. His hospital was a small frame building, his equipment a wastebasketful of instruments salvaged from his training at Johns Hopkins. To this primitive place he brought his young wife and infant daughter and began the work that has claimed his energies and devotion for twenty-five years. Patients thronged for treatment, and when a larger hospital was needed, Dr. Seagrave, his family, friends, Chinese coolies and even nurses built one out of cobblestones with their own hands. Through the years Dr. Seagrave trained native girls—Karen, Shan, Kachin and a half-dozen other races— to be nurses whose abilities astonished all who came to know them.

Then came the war. Dr. Seagrave was commissioned in the U.S. Medical Corps, formed a mobile medical unit, organized emergency ambulance service, and put field hospitals where they were needed. Through days and nights of Japanese bombing he and his nurses cared for the wounded until the order came to retreat and the Seagrave unit joined General Stilwell's march on foot out of Burma into India.

This was the story told in *Burma Surgeon*. In its sequel, *Burma Surgeon Returns*, Dr. Seagrave told of the hard-fought campaign to retake Burma, of the further adventures of his medical unit and the achievements of the brave little nurses as they carried on their arduous service in casualty clearing stations, always longing for the day when they would see their home again and be reunited with the people they loved. At last the enemy was driven out of Burma, the "Burma Surgeon" and his unit returned to Namkham and the hospital in the hills entered on a decade that was to be filled with dramatic events.

The story that follows tells of that eventful decade.

1

After the War

TEN YEARS have passed since General Stilwell and his divisions returned to Burma and regained the country in which they had "taken a hell of a licking" at the hands of the Japanese in 1942. With Stilwell I had marched out of Burma at the head of my hospital unit, through the jungle and over the hills to India, in what has become one of the famous retreats of history. And with that hospital unit—including the nurses I had trained at Namkham—I took the road back with the conquering army in 1944 and 1945.

Much has happened to Burma during the ten years that have passed since that return. Burma has been often in the news, and the news has not always been truthful. I wish I could tell the story of Burma during the years just past. It could not be a complete picture by any means. A great deal has happened which I have not seen, or have been unable to understand. My picture of Burma would, however, be seen through the eyes of an American doctor who loves Burma as he loves America. It would of necessity include the vicissitudes of the life he has lived, would contain some of the darker and more sombre shades so the brighter, vivid colors would stand out. A true story of Burma, too, would have to show the difficulties and trials through which Burma has gone, or the foreigner would not appreciate what Burma has accomplished and is accomplishing.

I cannot tell the whole story. But I can show some part of it by telling what has happened to me in the Burma of these most recent years—the trials and difficulties I have encountered, along with the people of Burma, and the happiness I feel in struggling—like them—to rebuild what has been destroyed.

My story begins in the spring of 1945, when the American battle to regain North Burma from the Japanese was drawing to a close. I knew that the Army would not be needing our medical unit much longer, and I, for my part, was growing more and more eager not only to get back to Namkham and my hospital there but to extend our services as far as we could throughout the surrounding area. I knew that the people of Burma had suffered intensely and would suffer still more as Burma was fought over for the second time. A great deal of reconstruction would be necessary, medically and educationally. And every able person who loved the country would be essential for recovery. I felt that I would be needed more in Burma than in any previous period of my career.

The decision as to my future came one day in April when the Chief of Civil Affairs Service suggested that my unit might be assigned to the Northern Shan States with myself as Chief Medical Officer. This was an assignment I could welcome with enthusiasm. I knew the Shan States like the back of my hand and had command of the two languages that were needed there. It was settled that I would begin the new job as soon as I returned from six weeks' leave for recuperation and visiting with my family in the United States.

The new post meant that I would have my headquarters at Taunggyi and from there would make surgical tours to all the towns and villages in the area—including, of course, my own home and hospital at Namkham.

What had happened to Namkham while the war was being fought? At first I knew only one thing: that the invading Japanese, when they occupied the town, had used the hospital buildings on the hill as barracks, thus inviting attack, with the result that the United States Air Force had done a pretty thorough job of bombing and destroying the hospital. I had even viewed the place through field glasses from a point several miles distant while we were on the road back, and could make out some of the damage. Then, as the Army pushed eastward toward the China border, the wonderful day came when I was able, with a few officers and some of the nurses, to make a short trip over to Namkham, which had just been taken by the 30th Division.

With intense excitement we approached our old home, over the broken and war-torn roads. Weeds choked the way, branches from bomb-shattered trees were strewn across the road. In the gateway was the crater of a thousand-pound bomb. Craters were everywhere. But the hospital itself was at least partially intact. The operating-room section and the women's wing were completely destroyed, but the men's wing was almost undamaged, and my office was untouched except for bullet holes. The iron roof had been torn completely off. The nurses' home had been hit but not much harmed, and other buildings were also usable. Everywhere was rubble and dirt.

We set to work at once to get the place cleaned up so we

could set up our unit in the sections still standing. Everybody helped. Shans and Kachins from nearby villages contributed free labor to clear away the rubbish. American bulldozers filled in all the big bomb craters, and the American engineers co-operated in so marvelous a fashion that thirty tons of cement actually disappeared through the back door of an Army storage warehouse, and some I-beams somehow strayed in just in time to support the upstairs floor of the operating section.

When the bombed wreckage was cleared away there was a single wall standing, which still supported one end of each of four of the queen roof trusses of the main building. The other ends of these trusses were some twenty feet lower on the ground, but the rafters and iron roofing still held them together. This was theoretically too big a job for my Shans and Kachins so I asked some G.I.'s to get help from the engineers and push the trusses back into position. After two days the Americans gave up. They didn't have a crane available to do the job, and the result was that I had to appeal to our Shan and Kachin coolies.

The Japanese had accidentally left my two house jacks behind. The coolies got those, borrowed all the jeep and truck jacks they could find when the owners were not looking, cut a lot of giant bamboos, and put the trusses, plus all the weight they were supporting, back up a few inches an hour until they were all in position. Then my two Shan masons rebuilt the front wall of the hospital until it again supported the trusses and the roof.

Almost every sheet of our old galvanized-iron roofs had been twisted and riddled by machine-gun bullets. "What do you intend to roof the hospital with, thatch?" asked my head carpenter.

"No. Use every sheet of old roofing that hasn't been shattered by bomb fragments," I replied.

"But they're full of bullet holes," he complained.

"Sure they are, so what? Use your brains. You've got brains."

While coolies hammered and twisted galvanized-iron sheets flat again, the carpenter wandered around the landscape, scratching his head, until he found a number of lead ingots the Japanese had hidden among the weeds. He melted the lead, poured it into forms which he had made himself, and turned out a lot of pencil-shaped cylinders just the diameter of an American heavy-machine-gun bullet. Half-inch lengths were then inserted in each of the thousands of bullet holes and hammered down on each side like rivets. A drop of tar completed the waterproofing.

Still there were not enough iron sheets for the roof, so the carpenter gathered together the sheets torn by bomb fragments and nailed them on in double layers, no two tears superimposed. The resulting roofs do not look as pretty as the lovely red-painted roofs of prewar days which so sharply outlined the hospital that from a distance of thirty miles on the road to Bhamo you could see it like a jewel against the background of the Shan State mountains. The present roofs look as if a perfect job of camouflage had been done on them. That is the proper way for a hospital to look now, when it is only one air-mile from the Bamboo Curtain of Communist China.

The nurses, thrilled to be back in their old quarters, worked at top speed to prepare to receive the patients already waiting to be transferred from the Army mobile unit. Soon we had three hundred beds occupied.

With the hospital a going concern, I had to leave to

rejoin my unit, still in action. The work of rebuilding went right on in my absence. This was because twenty years ago I had taken some ordinary Shan coolies with brains and had taught them to make river rock into a hospital. They would do excellent work, I knew, even when not continually supervised.

In a few months the battle for North Burma was over and my assignment as Chief Medical Officer of the Northern Shan States took effect. Delighted as I was with this new assignment, I was naturally concerned about the work to be carried on at Namkham while I would be at my headquarters at Taunggyi or making surgical tours from there to other points. This problem was soon solved.

I had an older sister named Grace who had graduated from the Johns Hopkins Medical School two years after I finished. Grace had come to Burma as a doctor assigned to the Ellen Mitchell Memorial Hospital at Moulmein in Southern Burma. She spoke Karen, which we had learned as children, as well as Burmese, and for one term she had been a medical missionary in Loikaw, capital of the Karenni States.

When Pearl Harbor struck, Grace was on furlough in the United States. After considerable difficulty she persuaded the Woman's American Baptist Foreign Mission Society to send her to Assam, India, where she would be as close to Burma as women were permitted to go. With the end of the fighting Grace was begging me to get her back into Burma to help in reconstruction. I had just enough influence to have her flown in to take over my job at Namkham while I was acting as Chief Medical Officer in Taunggyi. This was the wisest move I ever made.

2

Heritage

THE DESIRE to serve Burma runs in my blood. I am the last of twenty-eight of my family who have spent their lives for Burma. When I called upon my sister Grace to come and take over my work at Namkham, it was simply adding another link to a long chain reaching back into the past.

Our forebears—two lines of them, the Vintons and the Haswells—came to Burma one hundred and twenty years ago to teach the Christian faith. And in all that span of time, there have always been Vintons and Haswells—and later, Seagraves—carrying on their work among the people. The children of this family, for three generations, had been born in Burma; then, following the family pattern, were sent to the United States to be educated; and when education was completed, or before if need arose, returned to Burma to take over the work from their elders.

I want to go back a little and tell a part of the story of my family because it seems not unlikely that what they did and what happened to them has had a certain bearing on what has happened to me in the years just past.

The founder of our line, as it relates to Burma, was my great-grandfather, Justus Hatch Vinton, born in 1806 in Wellington, Connecticut, a direct descendant of one John

Vinton who came to Lynn, Massachusetts, in 1620. When Justus grew to manhood, he decided to give himself to the Christian ministry. Most young men then burning with religious fervor planned on following the frontier west across the future states. So did Justus until he met another New Englander, the pioneer missionary Adoniram Judson. Having been in Burma since 1812, Adoniram Judson had been greatly popularizing Burma as a country full of opportunities for the Christian faith, with hard work and difficulties to match. Young Justus weighed the needs and difficulties of following the American frontier with those of going to Burma and decided Burma was the harder job; he forthwith announced his intention of going there as soon as he could take his college work at Madison University —now Colgate University—in Hamilton, New York. The reason Justus chose Burma should be noted, as that reason crops up in generation after generation.

Growing up near Justus in Connecticut was a girl named Callista Holman. Callista at the beginning of her young womanhood seemed about to depart this life as a result of a lung condition—without benefit of baptism by immersion. This was a dreadful fate for an ardent Baptist in a land that was such a hotbed of ardent Baptists as was Connecticut in those days. She demanded that she be baptized, lung condition and all, despite the fact that the weather was extremely cold and immersion took place out of doors. Her pastor finally gave up and immersed her to such effect that Callista's health improved from that hour and she was able, in 1834, to marry the aforesaid Justus Hatch Vinton.

Justus knew not one thing about the many races of Burma and had no reason for choosing to serve one race rather than another. The choice was made for him. When the American Baptist Mission heard that Justus intended to come to Burma they appointed him forthwith as a missionary to the Karens, with headquarters at Moulmein. Justus and Callista with one accord set about studying the Karen language and actually became fluent in it while they were still in America.

That was in 1834. Justus Vinton and his wife Callista, after a journey of five and a half months, arrived in Moulmein, the large city where two other rivers join the Salween near its mouth. It is still a great city. Nearer the mouth of the Salween was Amherst, the big British administration center and fort.

The American Baptist missions at Moulmein and at Amherst were established to serve the Burmese—that is, the people of the great central plain of the Burma peninsula, whose kings ruled from Mandalay, and whose language was taught to all. The other races of Burma—Karens, Kachins, Shans and a half-dozen others—were distributed around the periphery of this central plain: eastward toward Siam, northeast toward the Chinese-Tibetan border, and northwest toward India. They were very different in origin and temperament and felt fiercely independent of one another. Among these, the Karens, deeply religious, were the most receptive to Christianity. The demand was great for missionaries who, like Justus and Callista Vinton, could speak the Karen language.

Justus and Callista made their home at Moulmein, but were in it as little as possible. Immediately on arrival they set out for the jungle to talk it over with the Karens in their own habitat, the villages in the hills. They did not know much about medicine, but they always carried along a lot of medicines and did what they could for any sick person they found, no matter of what race or religion. Another of their traits was that they refused to buy "rice Christians," men and women who consent to become Christians because they expect missionaries to feed them, support them and make it financially profitable for them to be Christians. People took the spiritual gifts the Vintons had to offer because they wanted them, not because they were bribed to accept them. The Vintons opened schools also, thus offending some American churches. This determination to make available to the people of Burma the things— religion, education, medicine, or democracy—which Americans enjoy and hold precious, persists in our family to this day.

Early in his missionary work, Justus had opened up a mission for the Karens in Rangoon, as a branch of his work at Moulmein. This had succeeded to a surprising degree in spite of the threats of the Burmese viceroy to shoot the first Karen he found that could read. In order to learn how to read, hundreds of Karens traveled at night across the jungles to Moulmein. As soon as they learned to read they went home carrying their Karen Bibles inside their shirts. At home they buried their Bibles in the daytime and dug them up at night, after placing guards around their houses. Such devotion made a strong appeal to Justus. He repeatedly asked permission to move to Rangoon, which he regarded as an important field. But permission was refused by two governments and by the American Baptist Mission. Things finally came to a head in 1852 when the Second Burmese War was fought, resulting in British rule in Rangoon. The defeated Burmese Army broke up into marauding bands, preying on the people and adding to the

misery of their lot. Justus heard of this misery, took the
bit in his teeth, and moved his family, bag and baggage, to
Rangoon. This move was regarded as a flagrant dereliction
by the American Baptist Mission Society and a formal vote
of censure was passed on great-grandfather Justus, cutting
him off completely from aid or recognition by the Mission.
This schism was to remain unbridged for twenty years.

Justus threw himself even more into his work after the
move to Rangoon. Famine followed the war, of course, and
the Burmese and Karens were soon starving and came to
Justus for help. He didn't have a cent, and he had no security
to offer either, but he went to some wealthy traders and
asked them if they would take a chance on a shipload of
rice, trusting to his honor to repay it. The traders said he
could have a dozen shiploads if he wished, whether he
could repay or not—provided only that Justus did the
distribution himself.

Justus distributed the rice right and left, without asking
for receipts or even listing the names of the recipients. Even
more shocking to many Christians in those days, he gave the
rice to whoever was starving, Karen or Burmese, Christian
or Buddhist. People dolefully prophesied that he would
never get back a cent, but as times improved every bit of
the money was repaid and the traders reimbursed.

Soon after the Vintons started work in Rangoon, Lord
Dalhousie, the Viceroy of India, gave Justus a grant of
land he had chosen out at Ahlone on a bluff facing west
across the mud flats to the Rangoon River, and Justus
started to build a house. He built it of teak in 1852, and it
still stands, being at present occupied by my sister Rachel.
It is now the oldest house standing in Rangoon. When the
house was completed Justus set about forming a Home

Mission Society among the Karens at Rangoon, and to them he made over all the property. (They still own it.) While Justus carried on his mission work, Callista opened a school which soon had an enrollment of two hundred and fifty, the first modern school in Burma north of Moulmein. From the start, this school was coeducational and largely self-supporting.

Justus went out touring the countryside on foot, on pony-back, and on elephants. Elephants were particularly valu-able when passing through thick jungle, for they could push a hole through almost anything. The only trouble was that frequently the elephant forgot to make the hole big enough for his passenger. At one camping place Justus de-cided to do a bit of Bible study and prepare his sermon while sitting under a tree. He soon became hot and thirsty and hopefully called out, "Fetch me some water, will you, somebody?" His elephant was the only one who heard, and the elephant promptly picked up a bucket, went to the stream, brought back a couple of gallons and doused it all over Justus, his Bible, and his sermon. That sermon thereby became a most Baptistic sermon.

By 1855 the Vintons were up against the most difficult thing any American with a mission has to undergo. Their son Brainerd was fifteen and must return to America to be educated and to fit himself to be an American citizen. This has been the policy of every generation. So Brainerd and his young sister were packed off on a ship—never to see their father again. Three years after the children left Burma, in 1858, Justus Vinton died of dysentery, contracted in his untiring labors.

Despite his success among the people, Justus had grieved deeply and worried over the split with the Missionary

Society. He had been censured by men whom he honored as great and good, men whom he had loved and continued to love. A year before he died he wrote the following letter to a friend in America:

"With regard to the vote of censure, though I have attempted nothing but in self-defense, I now regret even that I should have done that; that I had not made this my only answer, 'I am doing a great work and cannot come down.' As for the future, I ask for nothing, I care for nothing but my work. I have no wrongs that I even wish to have redressed."

I had never read this letter when, in October, 1949, I wrote one almost exactly like it. It was not until April, 1951, that I came on great-grandfather Vinton's letter in a book published in 1880.

Callista Vinton carried on after her husband's death, but it was quite a job for a lone woman. It was necessary, then, for son Brainerd to give up his plans for a seminary course. Immediately after graduating from Madison University, at twenty-one years of age, he returned to Burma. He brought with him his newlywed bride, Julia Ann Eliza Haswell.

Julia Ann Eliza Haswell was not only Brainerd's bride—she was his childhood playmate. Her parents, like his own, were American Baptist missionaries, living in Amherst, Burma. There Julia was born.

A look back at Grandmother Julia's family—the Haswells—again shows a sturdy Americanism. This family, too, had its origin in Colonial New England. Anthony Haswell came to Massachusetts in 1756 at the age of twelve and was apprenticed to a potter. He wrote songs for the Sons of Liberty and served in the Continental Army at Boston, Dorchester Heights, and White Plains. Somewhere along the line Benjamin Franklin turned him from pottery to printing, and he established the Vermont *Gazette*, the first newspaper published in Vermont, and became the first Postmaster General of Vermont while it was still a territory in 1784. In the new United States his editorials were so hot that the Federal Government threw him into jail until he should pay a fine of five hundred dollars—an enormous sum in those days. After he had spent months in jail his friends insisted on paying his fine and dragged him in a cart triumphantly through the streets of Bennington. Years after his death, the Congress of the United States of America passed a law returning the five hundred dollars, with interest, to Anthony's heirs. It arrived a little late to do Anthony much good, but it got me through Johns Hopkins.

Besides his editorials, Anthony produced a son, James Madison Haswell, my other missionary great-grandfather. Left an orphan at six, James surmounted various trials and tribulations, and eventually deciding to educate himself a bit, also went to Madison University in Hamilton, New York. After he had been there three years, the American Baptist Mission asked him to go to Burma to help Adoniram Judson with his Burmese work. He took his young wife, Jane Matilda Mason, to Burma and settled down at Amherst at the mouth of the Salween. And there young Julia Haswell spent her childhood.

A few years after Brainerd, with Julia, came home to Burma, his mother Callista died. Brainerd was now The Vinton. He took over the mission work from his mother and father, but although he received some aid from the churches in Connecticut, he had to support himself with business on the side. It was not until 1866 that the American Baptist Mission in Burma asked Brainerd to forgive and forget, and he rejoined them. In 1872 (twenty years after Justus had moved to Rangoon) this reunion was confirmed by the Society in America. Brainerd was the father of four children; three boys, George, Herbert, and Sumner, and a girl, my mother, Alice.

By 1886 the situation in Burma was again deteriorating rapidly. Endless bands of dacoits (armed robbers) were roaming the countryside, and the British could do little about them. Administration of the country became impossible. The government asked Brainerd to recruit soldiers and the situation improved, but Brainerd paid the price, and early the following year he died—also by acute dysentery acquired in the performance of his duties.

New blood was needed, and new blood was ready and willing. My mother Alice Vinton while at college (again Madison University) had done a bit of missionary work on a classmate, Albert Ernest Seagrave, and persuaded him that she and Burma were the most desirable things in the world. At the time of her father's death, she was taking her Medical School work in the Woman's Medical School in Philadelphia, and Albert was studying in Crozier Theological Seminary. When Albert finished his seminary training the couple left America—the first of the family to make their journey to Burma by steamer instead of a sailing vessel— and reached Rangoon in 1889.

When they arrived in Rangoon, Grandmother Julia called

my father in and made him a speech which I think showed a doubt not worthy of the man my mother had selected to carry on the family traditions.

"There are only two kinds of missionaries," she said, "talkers and doers. Which are you going to be?"

"A doer," said Father promptly, and he kept his word. He could easily have been both, because he had a tongue of gold. Father became the builder of the family. It started with the Karens who, saddened by the death of Brainerd, wished to perpetuate the name of Vinton in the form of a Memorial church. When Father arrived in Burma he was designated to build it. It took fifteen years to build it, and cost $3300—all raised by the Karens. This got Father off to an early start. He put up most of the buildings on the compound, including a brick high-school building and a tremendous girls' dormitory, his crowning achievement. All Father's buildings were brick; all mine were stone. But Father did a lot in addition to his regular mission work, which was educational as well as evangelical from the start. He supervised the foreign mission work the Karens of Rangoon were doing for the Karens in Siam by footing it there twice. And he made a trip for the Mission on foot right across the northwest frontier of Burma, over the Naga Hills to Assam.

The Karen Home Mission Society founded by great-grandfather Vinton finally broke up into two groups, each fighting for control and neither recognizing the other. Not even Father's tact and tongue of gold could accomplish anything with men fighting for personal aggrandizement. Father was completely broken up over the fight, which went on for years, and in 1931 a coronary occlusion caused his death.

My father's three children—myself and my sisters Rachel

and Grace—had been educated in America and had all three returned to serve Burma. Of these only the eldest, Rachel, had trained as an educational missionary and so she alone was assigned to Karen work in the Vinton-Seagrave mission at Rangoon. Grace and I elected to study medicine, feeling that our special talents were needed for all the Burmese races, not just for Karens. Grace was assigned to Moulmein to continue the work begun by the Haswell branch of the family for the Burmese, and I was assigned to Namkham in the far north. Our affection was for all of Burma. It had been bred into us by three previous generations.

3

Into the Shan States

On MY return from America in 1945, I set out to take up my duties as Chief Medical Officer in Taunggyi. The only way to get there was roundabout through Maymyo, Mandalay, Meiktila, and Kalaw.

The entire road was a mess. The destruction of towns, villages, and bridges was heartbreaking. Mandalay and Meiktila would have been unrecognizable except for geographical landmarks. Thazi had almost ceased to exist. Most Americans have never seen comparable destruction; our last four wars have been fought on foreign soil. Burma had been fought over twice, having first been destroyed by Japanese and then by Americans, British, and Chinese.

Heretofore my activities in Burma had been confined to the neighborhood of Namkham. Now I was to be concerned with the great stretch of territory covered by the Shan States, some knowledge of whose terrain may be helpful to the reader. Let us start at the north and proceed clockwise.

On the northern tip of Burma there is an area bounded by Tibet, but that tip is almost inaccessible because of very high mountains. These are part of the Hump that caused the death of so many American airmen during the war. On the northeast lies the Yunnan Province of China. On the east there is a common border with the province of Laos in French Indo-China and then with Thailand, which borders Burma all the way south from the Kengtung Shan State to the narrow bit of Thai isthmus which separates Burma from the Malay States. On the south there is the Gulf of Martaban between Rangoon and Moulmein and on the west the great Bay of Bengal, both of them parts of the Indian Ocean. Finally on the northwest there is Chittagong, a province of Pakistan, and Assam, a province of India.

Burma Proper, the home of twelve million Burmese and almost a million and a half Karens, consists of the great plains of the Irrawaddi and the Sittang and the coastal strip of Tenasserim down almost to the Malay peninsula. This is the Burma that was always ruled by the Burmese kings. It usually includes in people's minds the Arakan coast of the Bay of Bengal south of Chittagong, the Arakanese and Burmese being closely related, although until the British conquest, Arakan was usually a separate kingdom.

Around Burma Proper, like a huge question mark, are the Frontier States of Burma. They are almost entirely mountainous and they abut on the foreign countries mentioned above, separating those countries from Burma Proper. Beginning with the west and proceeding clockwise these Frontier States are the Chin and Naga Hills through which the British, American, and Chinese armies attacked when they drove the Japanese out of Burma; the present Kachin State; the Kachin substate of Momeik Shan State; the Kachin substate of North Hsenwi Shan State; the Shan State itself; the Wa States; the Karenni State;

and the Salween District, which is almost all the "state" the Karens have yet been given.

The people of these states have different origins and are of very different natures. The Kachins are stocky and strong, and are fierce fighters; they make the best soldiers of all the Burma races. The Shans came originally from southern China. They have been civilized for a thousand years. They had kings of their own and built walled cities and developed their own literature. Shan women are the most beautiful in Burma. The Karens are mountain people. Burmese kings subjugated them and treated them as inferiors. The Karens were always very religious and took eagerly to Christianity, which has become their national religion. They are kind and gentle as a people; Karen women make up the bulk of the nurses in Burma.

Namkham, where my adult life has been spent in medical work, is an overgrown village in the great Shweli River plain. It is on the border of five different states—the Kachin State, the Kachin substate of Momeik, the Kachin substate of North Hsenwi, and the Mongmao and Chefang states of Yunnan province in Communist China. The borders of four of these five states are within four miles of our hospital. The Shweli valley itself is Shan, and we are under the jurisdiction of the Shan sawbwa (prince) of Hsenwi State and therefore of the Shan State Government. But we are surrounded on three sides by Kachins. The nearest big towns are Bhamo, 72 miles by motor road to the northwest in the Kachin State, and Lashio, 132 miles by the Burma Road to the south. The Ledo or Stilwell Road, built from Assam by the U. S. Army during the war, passes right in front of our hospital to join the main Burma Road 25 miles away at

Mong Yu. And from Mong Yu it is perhaps 20 miles to Kyukok, where the Burma Road crosses the border into China.

Originally I did not choose Namkham as the site for my labors. I had it thrust upon me, and for some months I was not happy at the choice. Nobody in the area believed in western medicine, and only the Kachins were willing to submit to surgery. There was no big money around to make the development of a hospital easy. But in a year I was completely sold on Namkham, and the longer I work here the more I am convinced that it is exactly the site for everything we have to offer.

Namkham certainly has beauty. The valley is a rich agricultural plain which grows the best-tasting rice in the world. Those parts of the floor of the valley which cannot be irrigated furnish excellent pasturage for cattle. The floor of the valley and the hillsides which make a bowl of it are as heavily populated as any area of similar size in the Shan State. Many Burmese insist that the Namkham women are the most beautiful in Burma, a country of very beautiful women. The women of Burma are just as beautiful and graceful as the much-praised women of Bali, though Burman women do not demonstrate that beauty so frankly.

The hospital at Namkham is not truly in Namkham at all but on the first foothill between the suburb of Nawng Sang and the Christian Shan village of Kawng Nawng Sang. From the hospital site the scenery is exquisite. One can see almost the entire oval valley, from the towns of Muse in the Shan State and Mong Mao in Communist China in the northeast to the town of Man Wing in the Kachin State to the southwest. China's Bamboo Curtain roughly follows the silvery ribbon of the Shweli River, the greatest tributary of the Irrawaddi on the east, as it meanders down the center of this valley.

Thousands upon thousands of Shans live on the floor of this plain, their villages and houses almost completely invisible because of the graceful clumps of bamboo which they plant for building purposes. The names they give their villages are almost as beautiful as the villages themselves. Namkham itself means "Golden Water" or "River of Gold." Nawng Sang is named after a mythical elephant on an equally mythical lake. The little village of Wing Hsa, immediately south of the hospital, is a memorial to the hopes of its founding fathers, who dignified their handiwork with the glorified title of "Pleasant City." The Shan village through which our hospital's water supply flows is called Pantholin, "the Plain of the Peanut." It is possible to see only four or five of the many villages in the mountains surrounding the plain, for the rest are hidden among the forests. Yet there are hundreds, inhabited by Kachins, Palaungs, Lisu, and indigenous Chinese.

The foothills and almost all the tributary valleys are terraced into rice fields. These terraced fields continue right to the banks of the Shweli River, precluding the possibility of monotony in scenery. At the end of the cold season they are grassed over. Then the spring plowing suddenly turns everything a rich brown. In June, just before the rainy season sets in, irrigation water floods the whole valley into a terraced lake while it is plowed and harrowed to receive into its fertile soil the rice plants which are to be transplanted from the nurseries springing up like little emerald islands everywhere. All the rice is transplanted by hand before the middle of July, and the valley is then a vast checkerboard of color in every conceivable shade of green, from the greenish yellow of the most recently transplanted rice to the rich dark green of the lucky fields which first received attention. No sooner is the entire valley the proper shade of dark green than the end of the rainy season brings about the reverse process, and the grain ripens, terrace by terrace, into the golden harvest and then into the yellow-brown of the reaped fields.

And with October come the sunsets. I have enjoyed the famed sunsets of four continents. I have enjoyed the sunsets of Burma from Myitkyina to Tavoy. A Burmese gentleman, who has seen almost as much of the world as I, once wrote a prose poem for a column in the Rangoon *Nation* describing the beauties of all Burma. He had to admit that for sunsets nothing compared to those seen across the Shweli River from the hills east of Namkham. I agree with him. The people of Burma know beauty, and they love it.

When I arrived at Taunggyi to report for duty I found that I was second in rank to Brigadier Bowerman and that he had assigned to me as Staff Captain—Executive Officer in U. S. Army parlance—a Captain Silgardo, who was a Catholic Indian from Portuguese Goa. From the time he had received his degree in medicine at Rangoon University, Dr. Silgardo had had administrative assignments in the army and he knew all there was to know about administration. I promptly took out my surgical scissors, cut all the red tape and gave him the administrative work (incidentally, this probably kept me from being court-martialed). Then I jumped in my jeep and spent all my time visiting the hospitals under my care.

Everywhere there was sickness. During the Japanese occupation epidemic diseases had gone out of control. Smallpox was rife, and only rarely was it possible to secure still-active smallpox vaccine. Whole villages were wiped out by the horrible form of bacillary dysentery in which only the Shan State seems to indulge. Plague was going strong. For these I had an excellent public-health man, Dr. Ba Nyan, a Shan, whom I regard as one of the best. The doctors under me were quite capable of handling the medical diseases. But the surgery! Since no surgery had been available for civilians during the occupation there were not only ordinary civilian conditions in the most advanced stages needing surgery but there were also the wounds of war. There were not only old wounds, but new wounds resulting from hand grenades, shells, and other explosives left behind every-where.

On this first tour I reached the barren, devastated area where the town of Laikha used to be on the very morning that three boys had been trying to roast a grenade over a wood fire. So I spent the whole afternoon cutting pieces of shrapnel out of those boys. This was interrupted by my attempts to give them artificial respiration when the doctor poured on too much chloroform. I was annoyed. Only two of the doctors under me had ever had a chance to work under an older surgeon after leaving medical school. From school they had been shipped off to out-of-the-way spots where they were entirely alone and where they found no difficulty at all in forgetting everything they had learned, parrotwise, in medical school. By the time seniority brought them back to the neighborhood of a more experienced doctor they had forgotten everything. Their medical and surgical knowledge had never found its way to their finger-tips. And it is your fingertips that do surgery. I was perfectly willing and eager to teach any of these men who might want to learn how to do surgery, but the idea of killing patients for teaching purposes seemed somewhat offensive!

There had been medical and surgical emergency conditions in the Shan State before the war, notably those caused by the building of the great Burma Road to China. In those days we had been asked to assist in caring for the health of tens of thousands of coolies and villagers in the area through which the road runs from Lashio to the border. Staffed by nurses and an occasional doctor, the small hospitals which we had organized had been very successful, for they were based on Namkham, and our staff made ambulance trips twice a week supervising the work of the hospitals, caring personally for the most severe cases, and bringing the operative patients back to Namkham.

The present emergency in 1945–1946 was many times as widespread and serious. To offset this we had the services of a much larger number of doctors as well as what the English call compounders—a sort of pharmacist's mate. And our war-wise nurses were very efficient indeed, for they had worked throughout the war with some of the finest surgeons in the United States Army and had frequently been privileged to visit great American hospitals and watch well-trained American nurses at work. Taunggyi and Namkham could serve as base hospitals. But now the distances were too great to transport surgical cases to these two base hospitals, for it was roughly four hundred miles north from Taunggyi to Namkham and the same distance from Taunggyi east to Kengtung. The surgery would have to be done in situ and left with the local medical assistants. Either that, or the needed surgery would never be done.

I decided to travel with the nucleus of my own surgical team—at least one skilled nurse as anesthetist and another as assistant, with a third whenever any spares were available. We could rotate the girls, since all our one-time U. S. Army girls could handle any job with credit. These surgical tours would bring relief from the ennui of their regular work, quite apart from the fact that none of our graduates can exist without hard work to brace her up. I announced this plan of mine to the doctors as I completed my tour.

On my first surgical tour with nurses I found that the young Indian doctor at Mong Kung had saved me a beautiful ovarian cyst. That tumor must have weighed sixty pounds, and to my horror, as I discovered later, it was an infected cyst. I asked the doctor if he wouldn't like to scrub with me; he said he would. He rolled up his sleeves a couple of turns, handled the soap a second, and announced he was all ready.

"Doctor," I said, "roll those sleeves up to your shoulders. Take this brush and scrub yourself properly. Do everything just like you see me doing it, won't you?"

"Yes, sir," he said, pulling his hands out of the bichloride of mercury and brushing the hair out of his eyes.

"Now, doctor, you didn't see me doing anything like that. Get your hands back into the bichloride of mercury and then when your gloves and gown are on, clasp your hands tight in front of you so they won't touch anything."

Then I started painting iodine over that great mountain of an abdomen.

We were operating on the verandah of the hospital. That was the only place where there was light enough to see, and the word must have spread through the town that the Old American Doctor was operating, for everyone was coming from the stalls and shops. Pretty soon we had a nice crowd gathered all over the verandah, on the rail, even perched in the branches of the trees. We always play to a full house in the Shan States. That is the only way to do it, for then people realize that surgery is science and not witchcraft, and soon the patients turn up from all sorts of out-of-the-way corners of the state, insisting on surgery.

I draped my patient, made an incision almost a foot and a half long, and began to wonder why my doctor wasn't helping me. When I had a chance to look up, there he was, perched on the rail along with the rest of the boys. I shrugged my shoulders and went ahead with the operation by myself, exchanging a couple of surreptitious winks with the nurses who were giving the anesthetic and boiling instruments. Finally I sewed the patient up again. After it was all over I helped the nurses carry the patient back to bed, went into the small pharmacy and sat down on a box of Epsom salts, shaking all over with weariness, the horrible smell of pus still pervading my nostrils. And I was still shaking and still nauseated when, an hour later, the nurses came in and told me they had scrubbed and packed all our instruments and supplies and were ready to move on to the next town.

But that doctor insisted we stop and have a nice lunch before leaving. It took more courage to negotiate the lunch than it had taken to negotiate the ovarian cyst. Finally we got away from both the patient and the lunch.

About ten days later I learned that the public-works engineers had repaired the bridge on the north-south Shan States road, so I decided to travel north to see how things were going, especially at Namkham. Since we had to pass through Mong Kung again it seemed a good idea to stop and ask the nice young Indian doctor just what day the woman had died. As my jeep drew into the hospital compound the lady herself came out onto the verandah to welcome me; the doctor said she had been walking all over the hospital ever since the day following the operation. She just could not die!

To me that is the wonderful thing about surgery as it has been developed in this day and age. You can operate on the most forlorn, neglected patients. You can work on a verandah, in a bazaar stall, under a big tree in the jungle, or standing in foul-smelling mud. Immediately after the operation you can turn your patient over to a man absolutely ignorant of surgery, come back in a couple of weeks and find your patient well. And we even lacked penicillin. All the penicillin we had seen in those days was the original green penicillin which had never been kept in a refrigerator and was already nine months past its expiration date—penicillin that the British Army had thrown away.

Just about this time we heard that the road to Kengtung was open at last, with a current-powered ferry at the Salween River. On the orders of my Meiktila colonel I had sent a young Mohammedan doctor there on foot, not realizing that there was already in Kengtung a good Burmese doctor who had stuck out the Japanese occupation. Now, to me Kengtung is one of the most romantic spots in Burma, and I made up many valid and strong reasons why I should go there immediately. And go there I did, with a good team.

It is a long, long way to Kengtung—the Texas of Burma. From the Salween the road is like a ledge, going up and down the most ridiculously steep gradients. By falling over precipices and killing themselves truck drivers have proved again and again that it is not the kind of road to drive with a good-looking girl in the front seat, and I had not only two very good-looking ones in the front seat—one of them Big Bawk, whom the G.I.'s used to call "The Shape"—but a couple in behind as well. It speaks well for my ability to concentrate that I have never dropped over a cliff on the Kengtung road. When the authorities announced the road was open they meant just that. They didn't mean that they had repaired the ruined bungalows. We slept by the side of the road, with or without a thatch roof over our heads and despite the horror of snakes which I have never been able to overcome.

On our arrival there were several operative cases waiting for me, one of them a wealthy Sino-Burman trader with positively the worst exophthalmic goiter I ever saw. His eyes were popping out of his head, and he had other symptoms to match. Why he did not die during the exacerbations that overtook him during the Japanese occupation, as his wife declared he should have done, I shall never know. And I had no time to prepare him for the operation except to fill him full of soda and glucose while he slept that night.

The new doctor claimed he was a surgical specialist so I thought I wouldn't have to teach him how to scrub, and I sent him and Bawk to get scrubbed up while one of the other nurses put the patient to sleep and I tried to calm my nerves. When I went in to scrub not only had the doctor finished scrubbing and putting on his gloves and gown but he was helping Bawk into her gown, tying the tapes behind and giving a few surreptitious pats to various somewhat prominent places. I was just ready to explode when Bawk caught my eye, winked, and grinned. So instead of exploding I got Bawk to hold his hands for him—in the bichloride basin—and I began to scrub.

By late afternoon all the operations were over, and my

goiter patient was rather more than alive. We climbed wearily into the jeep and drove all night back towards the Salween. It is much safer to drive the Kengtung road at night. There is much less danger of bumping into someone going around a corner. Besides, all the girls sang—everything from hymns to "Alouette" and the "Marine Song"—especially Bawk, who has the fullest, sweetest voice of any Kachin I know. It was a great and glorious occasion.

So was my next trip to Kengtung. Not only had my goiter patient not died, but he had a twenty-five-course Chinese banquet prepared in my honor. He was rather offended because I wouldn't let him give me a gigantic fee, but I was on my U. S. Army salary still and would not let even the British pay me.

4

Sawbwas

NEVER have I seen so desolate a country as the Karenni State right after the last Japanese were driven out. When I made my first trip a few Japs were still sniping at cars. The Karenni States have never been really conquered by anyone. The Burmese kings finally quit trying. The British could have done it by killing every last Karenni but they didn't need to, for Karenni entered British Burma by voluntary treaty, just as Nepal had joined British India. Nor did the Japs conquer Karenni. Whenever they appeared, the Karennis disappeared into the woods and ambushed them. It made the Japs so angry that they destroyed everything they could reach. There was not one village left on the road, and for a few months there was no cultivation to be seen. Then Sao Shwe, the young sawbwa of the middle Karenni State of Kyebogyi,* appeared on the motor road at a place which he called Prussoe, where he had decided to set up his capital. The original capital was too far away in the woods.

Sao Shwe was a man after my own heart. I have never seen anything like the growth of that brand-new town. Before the school building was completed and even before it was properly roofed he had a school going out of his own

* Not to be confused with Sao Shwe Thaike, the first president of Burma.

funds. The school had no sooner been built than he had a temporary grass-shack hospital to which I had to assign a compounder from a unit far away which didn't need him. A year later Sao Shwe had put up some permanent staff buildings for a new hospital, and six months after that he was building a cement tile hospital. This was before he got himself messed up with the insurrection. Now he is reported as having been killed in action. When you think of the thousands of men of Sao Shwe's inherent ability who have ruined themselves and their country by joining in these multicolored rebellions against the Government of Burma instead of finding a basis of co-operation for the good of the country you are simply overwhelmed with grief.

From all this the reader might imagine that my headquarters at Taunggyi never saw me. The fact is, I was there most of the time, signing anything Dr. Silgardo put in front of me and doing operations in the hospital which the others wouldn't undertake, mostly gynecological operations. At this writing, people who are supposed to be informed tell me I am almost the only practicing surgical gynecologist for major operations in Burma, a country which needs hundreds of surgical gynecologists.

Before long the Shans and the Inthas who live just southwest of Taunggyi around Inle Lake in Yawngwhe State learned who was in Taunggyi. Immediately they began to drag up the most pitiful patients, not only gynecological cases but tremendous thyroid adenomas as well. Undoubtedly my worst case was the largest intraligamentary cyst of the ovary I have ever seen. As it grew into the abdomen the tumor had dissected up a good half of the pelvic peritoneum. I had never seen another surgeon handle anything like this, so I sutured the peritoneum back down into the pelvis as well as I could and marsupialized where I couldn't suture. The patient still brings me presents of fruit every time I visit Yawngwhe.

The English Dr. Gurney who had served with us throughout the war now returned to us as a British major. So I shipped my good associate Dr. Ba Saw back to do the surgery at Namkham and turned Taunggyi over to Gurney. It is a beautiful thing to watch Gurney do surgery, for his hands are beautiful surgeon's hands, not spadelike hands such as mine. But he slipped the big goiters and the gynecological cases over to me when I wasn't looking. The most difficult case he gave me was a woman who had been delivered by an impatient doctor. He had torn the cervix into the bladder with a forceps delivery before the cervix was fully dilated. Dr. Gurney had had a try but couldn't figure out where to begin and had put the patient to bed to wait for me. It took me three hours to repair that bladder and I had a kink in my neck for a week thereafter.

Almost simultaneously with Dr. Gurney's arrival the big bridge on the road from Taunggyi north to Lawksawk State was finally repaired, and I decided to visit the place and see what could be done. On our first arrival at Taunggyi I had sent our little princess Louise there, since that was her home state. Thereupon she developed quite a dispensary practice, even sending some operative patients down to Taunggyi. Then my Colonel had objected, since Lawksawk deserved a doctor, and I had had to send there a retired private practitioner who didn't like the way the military Government was throwing him around.

I paid a courtesy call on the sawbwa, who thought I might like to take a look at his daughter who "had malaria." She was dying of typhoid and had just had a big hemorrhage. I gave up the plans for the rest of my tour, asked the sawbwa to locate immediately all the faithful old retainers who might be willing to donate blood, and rushed back to Taunggyi. Gurney set off at once with Grandma Naomi as assistant and Big Bawk with her laboratory, found a blood donor who matched, and the girl began to get well from that hour.

During the seven months I was Chief Medical Officer under the British Military Administration there were some states where we could not accomplish anything. The reason was that the local doctors were unwilling to co-operate for fear they would lose prestige if the townspeople discovered there were other doctors who could cure them when their local doctors could not. This psychology is all reverse psychology. The doctors that co-operated received plenty of reflected glory and were soon favorites in their states. Those that failed to co-operate got no prestige at all, reflected or otherwise.

Mongnai was one of the places where at first it was almost impossible to do any good. Even the sawbwa seemed not to care, apparently because he was sick. Finally the Resident Commissioner of the Southern Shan States called me to his office and told me he was worried to death about the old sawbwa of Mongnai: He wouldn't come to Taunggyi and he wouldn't let any other doctor touch him but me. Would I please go to see him?

Now, sawbwas like to have their doctor live right in the palace with them when they are sick and stay with them until they are well. According to the Commissioner, Mongnai had at least six major illnesses (he did have four) and

I didn't want to spend the rest of my life sitting in his palace, so I took Louise along. Since she was entitled to use the term *Sao*, which means prince or princess, before her name, the sawbwa might let her take care of him.

When I reached the palace it was worse than I had anticipated. The sawbwa had changed his mind about wanting me and was poisoning himself with Shan medicine. It took me an hour to talk my way into his heart far enough for him to take off his shirt. I left a couple of pages of instructions for Louise, whose family tree had been thoroughly investigated by the time I finished my examination, and next morning was off.

When I came back ten days later Louise was one of the family and I was adopted, for the old man was able to sit on the verandah and even walk around a bit. Two years later while I was in America on a lecture tour he died, but meanwhile he advertised the hospital. We placed two good nurses there, one of them the Ruby Thaw who is now in Philadelphia, and every time I visited Mongnai thereafter, I found a long line of patients waiting to be examined and six or eight major operations to be performed.

All these states where we were really able to accomplish a lot were in the Southern Shan States. All but Hsipaw. I visited all the northern states, but everyone was enjoying "good health" and no one needed surgical attention. Extraordinary! No one was sick except in Hsipaw, where Dr. San Yee was, and in nearby Kyaukme, where there was a most charming Shan doctor named Hkun Saw. Hkun Saw thought that if as big a man as San Yee could acquire more prestige by letting me help him so could he. So there were always operations at Kyaukme if Hkun Saw knew I was coming.

After the operations, one night, while driving back from Kyaukme to Hsipaw, I looked up, just as I came to the underpass under the railway line; there was a full-grown tiger, looking down at me from the rail bridge. I am glad he was not hungry at the time.

San Yee was a good surgeon himself, so I had only the exceptional things left for me. Among these were cataracts. I tried to beg off, since I had no good cataract knives, nothing but a couple of rusty Graefe knives with points like crochet hooks. But San Yee insisted that the poor patients would take any kind of a chance to get their sight and suggested that I use a safety-razor blade. It sounded like a good idea. I had a couple of cheap bazaar blades which we grasped in clamps and fractured on the diagonal so as to get a sharp point, but the steel was so soft and flexible that it wouldn't push through the eyeball. Finally I gave up in disgust, took my one and only Gillette Blue Blade that I was hoping to save for my own chin, and fractured that. Then we did a large number of cataracts successfully until I finally managed to import some Graefe knives from America.

Though Burmese patients seem to thrive on "wastebasket" surgery, I am tired of being a wastebasket surgeon. Someday before I die, I should like, just once, to do a major operation at Namkham with every modern facility, with none but the most complete set of brand-new American instruments in an absolutely modern hospital and with no worry about costs. However, it might not be good for me. I should probably have a coronary occlusion and drop dead from shock.

While I was acting as Chief Medical Officer during the military administration, I had to keep reminding myself forcefully that this was not only the best but also the only way I could be of service to Burma at that time. I disliked Government service for myself as much as I had hated the red tape of the Army. My feeling increased when my boss, Brigadier Bowerman, became so impatient with the military government's actions that he suddenly remembered a knee stiff from a shrapnel wound of World War I and persuaded a medical board to retire him from his job as chief in the administration of the Shan and Karenni States. In spite of the loss of my Brigadier, my love for Burma made me stay on the job.

My job permitted me to help the whole Shan and Karenni State, and our hospital at Namkham was one of the military administration's system of hospitals under me. The result was that an occasional visit to Namkham was part of my job and the only part—aside from the opportunity of becoming intimately acquainted with the medical conditions of the entire Shan State—which compensated me for the misery of absolute Government control of all my actions.

Namkham was the last stop on every swing through the Northern Shan States. Once we passed Lashio on our way north, something seemed to happen to each member of our team, for there we began to meet Americans, who were closing out the different U. S. Army installations. As an American jeep whizzed by us on its way to Lashio, Emily, my senior nurse, and the other girls on the team almost lost their balance leaning out of my jeep to watch the G.I.'s go by. When they were out of sight Emily turned and sighed.

"Those were Americans. My, didn't they look good!"

They were a Graves Registration team, and they did look good.

For my part I was always thrilled with the fact that now only a few miles separated us from Namkham and the hundreds of Americans still in our valley, and I drove like a fifteen-year-old in a hot-rod, my eyes on the lookout for mischief. On this trip with Emily I found it. A couple of miles beyond the American jeep I saw a flock of wild fowl on the left edge of the tarmac. When they heard the jeep the rooster and his wives did not take off for the jungle but tried to outfly me along the road. Now, this is a thing no bird can do when I am on my way back to Namkham. They struggled so hard for speed that they made altitude slowly, and I shouted to the team:

"I'll catch a wild fowl for you."

"Two bits you don't," said Emily.

"Done!" I said, and made a pass at a hen with my left hand.

"See, you lost," said Emily.

"Not quite," I replied, "you owe me one bit because I've got part of the hen in my hand."

Then I opened my hand to display two tail feathers, but I had startled the hen so badly that she had had an accident in my hand and I had to stop at the next stream to wash. How many years will it take me to live that one down?

At Namkham I found that the Ordnance installation at the junction of the Ledo and Burma Roads was being dismantled, and it was rumored that they were blowing up such jeep and truck equipment as they would not be able to transport back to India. I hurriedly managed to squeeze in a trip to the junction and found that on my arrival several trucks were indeed being dynamited. I was not too late, however, to secure a lot of used tires and even some unused spare parts. Our vehicles are still running on those tires, seven and a half years later. If only I could have been there a few days earlier! Then I had to report to Combat Command Headquarters in Bhamo. The day before I reached there, three thousand used G.I. blankets had been burned, allegedly because of some agreement between the U. S. Army and the British. If I could have arrived a day earlier, the Army would have been glad to turn them over to an American lieutenant colonel, and the British would not have objected to *my* using them in a hospital for the Burmese.

Other things happened, however, which were even less excusable. I learned on my trip to Ledo for my final discharge papers that the Evacuation Hospital at Shingbwiyang had dumped a great deal of its precious equipment into a ravine and bulldozed earth over it. And yet, here was our American hospital unit, with almost no equipment, staying on in Burma; we would have trucked the equipment away gladly and silently if we had only known, even, if so specified, on moonless nights. I could have gotten away with it because my prestige was high at the time with both the Burmese and the English. This was back in early 1946.

At Ledo I learned of a missionary who was doing what I would love to have done had I not been so busy with reconstruction work in Burma. He was loitering around the different American installations, picking up equipment by the truckload as each unit pulled out for the States. I wonder if I would have been of more real value to Burma if I had imitated him instead of bucking the line in Burma throughout the medical emergency of those crucial months.

I must be a very old-fashioned American. I cannot tolerate waste. I had to learn very early in World War II to regard very costly equipment as expendable. We destroyed our trucks and equipment as we marched out of Burma on foot with General Stilwell. It hurt, but we were in a very real hurry, and anything we left undestroyed would have helped the enemy in his fight against us. When we came back into Burma ten years ago we were also in a hurry and could not always carry everything along with us as we moved forward with limited transportation facilities. Still, we took pains to see that everything we left behind fell into the hands of friendly Burmans who had been helpful in our fight against the Japanese.

We Americans suffer from a "rich" complex. We abandon and destroy things right and left, assuming that our resources are unlimited. If time is of the essence and we must abandon things, by all means let us abandon them to the welfare of our friends, and not destroy them. How often I have wished the engineers on the little airstrip behind our hospital had left a gravestone over the grave of a baby bulldozer they are said to have buried there. I would have torn up the *Requiescat in Pace* sign and resurrected the baby bulldozer for another short lifetime of service to Burma.

5

Government Doctor

When Sao Shwe Thaike ("Prince Golden Nest") invited me down to the *Thadingyut* Feast of Lights I had my first opportunity to talk with him about postwar conditions. Later, when the Union of Burma was achieved, he became the first president. All the other guests had been invited for the first day of the celebration, when the ancient gods are brought out of their permanent home to make a tour of the lake villages. On the final day, when the gods are taken home again for another year, I was the only guest. And so I had the future first president and his *mahadevi* (chief queen) all to myself in their great barge. This was a huge, flat-bottomed, square-ended boat with a comfortable cabin and a front deck big enough for guests to sit and enjoy the view. When I climbed aboard I looked for a motor but saw none. As it turned out, there was a much more romantic way of propelling the boat.

The Inthas are a curious anomaly in the Shan States. They are like no other group in Burma but the Tavoyans, a very early branch of the Burmans who engage in sea-fishing on the Tenasserim Coast around Tavoy not far from Malaya, and speak a sort of Chaucerian Burmese. The Tavoyan and Intha languages are very similar. The only explanation that makes sense is that hundreds of years ago some conquering Burmese king dragged a lot of Tavoyans up from Tenasserim and deposited them a thousand miles away on Inle Lake in the Shan State. These Inthas are the hardest-working people in Burma. Every village has its village industry, the noise of which is heard from early morning until late at night. Also they are the great merchants and traders. During the war they were the first to recognize that the Japanese occupation would mean that Burma would soon be starved of salable goods. So they went down to Rangoon, bought up everything in sight, especially textiles, and carted them off to the Lake. By the end of the occupation the Burmese had to reverse this process and go to the Lake to buy back some of their own textiles. The Inthas did not lose on the deal. They never do.

One of the most fascinating things about the Inthas is the way they row their dugouts. Some of these are really enormous, but some are so tiny as to be almost invisible at any distance. The oarsman stands on one leg, wraps the other around the shaft of a long oar, and then using the hip as a fulcrum, he gets a tremendous sweep forward. In all my experience I have only once seen an Intha lose his balance and fall into the water. That was the day I was in Sao Shwe Thaike's barge, which was towed by four huge dugouts, each manned by about twenty-five leg-rowers. They hitched their dugouts on in front and thus pulled the barge across the lake to the rendezvous.

Inle Lake is much bigger than it looks, for its shallows are covered by floating islands, and you do not realize at first that the lake is under them. Not so long ago the lake must have extended about twenty miles farther north than it does now, but silting has taken place, which in the last forty or fifty years has been greatly expedited by the pernicious water hyacinth which clogs every stream in Burma. As a boy I used to travel all over the Irrawaddi delta and I would surely have remembered the floating hyacinth, if it had been at all common, because the flowers are so lovely. Of recent years, however, to appreciate its beauty you have to close your minds to its nuisance value.

The story goes that some American lady-tourist was so fascinated by the floating hyacinths she saw on some South Sea island that she took a few plants on board ship with her and deposited a plant here and there in each of the countries she later visited. If that story is true she certainly messed up Burma for all time unless someone can find some way to turn these hyacinths into fertilizer. Although Yawng-whe town used to be on the shore of Inle Lake, you now have to go through miles of hyacinths, white and red water lilies, pink lotus, and just plain ordinary floating islands until you get to the open lake. In boats powered by outboard motors, which I later used on my surgical tours, the boat-men were continually untangling the propeller from the hyacinths, and you made haste very slowly indeed. But Sao Shwe Thaike's barge had no such trouble because it was propelled by leg power and the hyacinths had been specially cleared from the main approach to the lake.

Everyone was in festive garb. It was interesting that, after they had kowtowed most effectively to the Sawbwa once, he started kidding back and forth with them all in a most democratic manner. It was an interesting mixture of feudalism and democracy. Soon we passed a canoe filled with yellow-robed Buddhist monks. This time it was the monks who sat bolt upright as if they didn't see a thing, and the Sawbwa who did the kowtowing.

At the rendezvous there were unbelievable numbers of

dugouts waiting for the races. Before the races, floats of beautifully decorated dugouts paraded past the royal barge. The one that took the prize was a boat fluttering from stem to stern with thousands upon thousands of Japanese-printed rupee notes whose face value would be about a million rupees and whose actual value was absolutely nil. They could not be used even for wrapping paper. As if they felt no resentment at all against the Japanese for making them lose all this money, the losers laughed at their misfortunes with the true spirit of sportsmanship.

Then the races began. The course was about one hundred yards, with the tape right in front of the royal barge. The races were for twenty-oared, fifty-oared, and one-hundred-oared boats. With so many men thrusting forward at once on the boat there had to be a handrail down the center to which the oarsmen could cling with one hand while with the other arm and one leg they rowed forward with tremendous power. The spectators roared in a way that would have done credit to a game between the Yankees and the Dodgers. Then came the last float in the middle of which, in a flower-bedecked barge, were the three gods. I saw them only from a distance, but they looked to be of great age and certainly must have been from the pre-Buddhist era of Burma. After the gods had been taken back into their monastery, everyone set out for home.

On this excursion I first described to Sao Shwe Thaike what we had been doing at Namkham towards medical reconstruction. I told him about the Kachin and Shan girls we had taken in for training. I mentioned the fact, too, that though a school for boys and girls in Myitkyina had been the first school to be reopened in Burma, we had been the second with the reopening of our own school at Namkham. This had made it possible for pupil nurses who had not completed pre-nurse training to do so on weekdays while they studied practical nursing in the hospital on Saturdays and Sundays. Also we gave half-time credit in the nurses' training school to girls who needed to study only English, and quarter-time credit to girls who had to study in school all day long. I explained that this was a substitute device to help the country carry on until doctors could be properly trained in numbers so that nurses could then do only the work for which they were properly intended. Sao Shwe Thaike appeared very interested. He asked me to let him know as soon as I thought we could accept more girls for training and said that he would send girls from his own state.

That time came in January, 1946. We had been alerted to be ready to turn over to the civilian authorities at a moment's notice. By then I had had quite enough of being a military government servant. As soon as I could turn over I wanted to get back to Namkham where I belonged, and really start the reconstruction of our hospital work and the training of nurses. Accepting a few girls who applied as private students and agreeing to take the girls that Yawngwhe, Mongnai, and Kengtung had selected, we arranged to have everyone gather in Taunggyi at the end of January in order that we might all go north to Namkham together.

The week before the exodus I was again in Kengtung. Just before operations began, a tiny Shan girl turned up. Her black eyes flashed so brightly you didn't need to ask her I.Q. She said the sawbwa had added her to the list of pupil nurses, but there was no transportation for her. Could she go back to Taunggyi in our jeep with the two Christian girls we had already arranged to take? I agreed, provided she would be ready, bag and baggage, at the hospital in the evening.

That evening, as soon as the operations were over, we piled everybody's baggage in the trailer on the top of our surgical instruments and supplies, and the two nurses climbed in with me in front. I was taking no chances on assigning seats to three strange women—not in the back of that jeep. I supposed that the Christian sisters would stand back out of courtesy and let the little Buddhist girl choose her seat first. But these Christian girls had other ideas. To them this was a Christian jeep—a well-baptized Baptist jeep. Therefore of course the Baptist girls had the right to the seats of honor. Shoving the little Buddhist girl to one side, they climbed in, taking the semicomfortable seats, one on each side of the forty-gallon gas tank. There was nothing left for the Buddhist girl but to climb in right on top of the gas tank, and there she sat, with her legs crossed in front of her, swaying this way and that all the way back over that ghastly road to Taunggyi.

Then the great morning arrived. There were about thirty-five new girls from the Southern Shan States waiting. My drivers drove out two of our huge army trucks, threw in all of the baggage, and the new girls climbed in on top. The graduate nurses and I brought up the rear in the jeep to pick up anyone who bounced off, and incidentally to breathe in tons of dust. Three days later we reached Namkham. After the girls recovered from the trip, I called them all into the nurses' ballroom and made a speech.

"Girls," I said, "this is not a jail. There isn't a single way we could lock you girls into your nurses' home if we wanted to, which we don't. You have bolts on the inside of the doors so you can bolt the wrong people out, but nothing on earth can keep you from unbolting the doors any time you so desire. We expect to treat you just like your fathers and mothers do at home, and from experience we have reason to expect that you will treat us like you do your own fathers and mothers.

"Now, this is a Christian hospital and we have Christian services, and I expect the Christian girls to go to those services. But most of you girls are Buddhist. If you would like to come to our Christian services at any time, please understand that you are invited and that we shall be delighted to have you. But no one will ever force you. On the other hand, there will be many occasions when you will want to go to Buddhist ceremonies in the town, and whenever you want to, you may. You don't need to ask for permission. All you have to do is tell one of the matrons where and when you are going so we can arrange the hospital work while you are away; and if you need transportation we will furnish it. Any Buddhist ceremonies commonly conducted in your homes you may conduct in the nurses' home to your hearts' content."

The girls said nothing, but you could see they did not believe a word of it.

A couple of months later came the great Thingyan Water Festival. This occurs in the hottest part of the year. In the old days they used to pour water over the images at the pagodas to cool them off. Also they poured water on one another. When this festival first began, if a girl was going to pour water onto a boy it was supposed to be perfumed water with rose petals floating on top; but the feast had degenerated as so many do—like our Hallowe'en—so that now they throw water at each other by the bucket and sometimes throw bucket and all.

On the big day of Thingyan I was really scared. I didn't want to be wet all day as I went about my duties in the hospital and taught my classes of nurses, so I was very careful to stay just as far as I could from the walls of the buildings, especially the two-story buildings, lest a sack of water come crashing down on my head. But the girls were just as good as gold—that is, until they came off duty in the afternoon at five. When I started from the classroom to go over to the mess hall, where Grace and I were still eating with the nurses as we did during the war, there they were, waiting for me. Two long rows of nurses were lined up on each side of the road to the mess hall; each girl had in her hand a basin of perfumed water with rose petals floating on the top. The first girl in the line, an Intha from Yawng-whe, dipped her fingertips into the water and bravely sprinkled a half-dozen drops on me, wondering how I would take it. Knowing that politeness wouldn't satisfy them, I snatched the basin out of her hand, doused the water all over her, getting her glorious long black hair sopping wet, and ran to the faucet in the garden for more. Then for an hour a wonderful time was had by all until the water was flowing out of my nose and ears.

Among the girls from the Northern Shan States were three from the Palaung state of Taungbaing. They were the first Palaung girls ever to come for training. At first I was delighted when I found they were Palaungs and then horribly disappointed when it appeared that they didn't have I.Q.'s sufficient to study nursing. All we could do was teach them midwifery by drilling it into them day in and day out. Eventually they made good midwives, but I was rather provoked at their sawbwa, whom I considered one of the four or five greatest. Then I found out what he was doing: The Palaungs are very strong Buddhists, especially the sawbwa. No Christian missionary of any denomination had ever been permitted to work in Taungbaing State. The sawbwa did not want his really good girls to be corrupted by being forced to study Christianity, so at first he had sent three poor-quality girls. His game was to see whether we treated them properly or not, and the girls had been sending in regular reports.

Soon after the Thingyan Festival I was in Taungbaing's capital, Namhsan. Here the sawbwa was unusually friendly. He had two more girls, he said, who would like to study nursing. Then he presented two of the finest girls we ever trained, girls who were leaders of the entire body of nurses, Christians and all. They have graduated now. One was put on duty in Lashio, the other was in the Wild Wa States holding down a job that no doctor would touch with a ten-foot pole. Doctors have, I believe, never been known to last in the Wild Wa States for more than six months.

But however good their work where they were sent, these two girls should have been allowed to work in Taungbaing as guaranteed in the contract signed by them with the Government. They were the first two qualified nurse-mid-wives ever to be trained from Taungbaing State, and that state needs its own girls if no other does. Its topography consists almost entirely of precipitous mountains; girls from other states just can't bear the loneliness and the unbe-lievably steep mountain roads. The only doctor was at the capital, and he never went out on call. One plain near Hsipaw used to be served on bazaar days by Dr. San Yee while he was there. But for the people in these mountain fast-nesses nothing at all was being done.

The excuse was that no work had ever been done out in Taungbaing State, therefore there was no position avail-able. But that's why these girls were trained—to make some sort of medical attention available to tens of thousands of people who had never had such attention before. There were plenty of girls from North Hsenwi and Hsipaw to go to places like the Wild Wa States. But the Palaungs of Taung-baing believe less in western medicine than any other race. They can be converted to modern medicine better by girls of their own race than by doctors of any race whatsoever. It grieved me that the two Palaung girls of the first rank served and fulfilled their promise to the Government out-side their own state, which needed them so badly.

There was a delay in turning over the medical work of the British Military Administration to the Civil Govern-ment until March, 1946. By that time I was frantic to go back to Namkham to stay, and Dr. Gurney was just as eager to return to his Bible Church Mission Society work at Pang-long. Then I heard there was to be a great conference in this very Panglong. Visitors had been invited not only from all the Shan States but from other frontier states as well. My good friend the sawbwa of Mong Pawn, who, although he was the sawbwa of a poor state, was introducing all sorts of modern agricultural methods into the country, asked me to address this conference on the existing medical conditions in the Frontier States and plans for improving those condi-tions.

Speeches were made by all sorts of people, but the two

chief speakers were from Burma Proper—the present Prime Minister U Nu (then Thakin Nu), who was there as a representative of Burma's national hero General Aung San, and U Saw, prewar Prime Minister of Burma, who was there representing himself. As far as I know, Thakin Nu made only one speech, of which I heard only the end, because I came next and was busy polishing up my own.

I made my speech in Burmese, Shan, and English, and it was translated into Taungthu. I pointed out that in the Frontier States at that time the five most important diseases in the order of their importance were malaria, goiter, dysentery, syphilis and gonorrhea, and that by reason of recent advances in medical knowledge all five could be wiped out very rapidly, provided the Government would make the necessary funds available. I referred to the statement made both by the British and the Burmans themselves that the people of Burma were a lazy lot, and declared that no race with a normal average hemoglobin content of sixty percent could do anything but act lazy. Any expenditure in capital outlay by the Government, I then urged, would soon be recovered because of the rapid improvement in the economic conditions and the standard of living which would immediately result from the improved health of the country.

I urged that all the states select the best young men they could find and make it financially possible for them to go through high school, college, and medical school in order that the country's starving need for good doctors might be satisfied with the utmost speed. As the best possible substitute and on a temporary basis I suggested that each state select the best girls available and send them for training as nurses. Meanwhile, using the graduate nurses that were available, hospitals should be maintained in every area for which no doctors could be secured. Such nurses could be supervised by regular tours of doctors fit to supervise them.

I pointed out how much easier it was for nurses to popularize modern medicine than for doctors; women could soon obtain the confidence of the all-important women and children—the people with the greatest need—and through them the confidence of the men, whereas doctors could get the confidence only of men and could do nothing with women. Then I suggested that as these nurses graduated each one could be put in charge of a little valley in a circle around a junior doctor who would supervise. Then several junior doctors could be supervised by a senior doctor in charge of the individual small state, and several of these senior doctors would be supervised, in turn, by a really good surgeon in charge of a district. This top surgeon's primary task would not be signing a lot of letters, but visiting, himself, all hospitals under him and making surgery and expert medical treatment available *in the place where the sick were*, rather than trying to force the sick to go hundreds of miles for their surgery, only to discover that their diseases were inoperable.

I reminded them that there had been no schools open for four years and that many superior girls had been unable to secure the education that would fit them for nurses' training. Then I described how we had handled that problem with the pupil-nurses from the Kachin and North Hsenwi States by giving them special tutoring in our own school—tutoring which had resulted in many girls being able to go up two grades in a year. Finally I urged in conclusion that the doctors occasionally be given leave for a period of from six months to two years so that they might take refresher courses and training in surgery under expert surgeons in Burma, in India, or in Western countries.

My speech made quite an impression, for in those days the Japanese occupation was still fresh in everyone's minds and the sawbwas—except perhaps one or two extremely selfish men—were vitally interested in the improvement of their states along every line. Jockeying for position in politics had not then become the style. The sawbwas, in fact, voluntarily relinquished one of their very much cherished rights and invited an equal number of commoners to sit with them in their Shan States Council.

6

Surgical Tours

Not long after my speech Sao Shwe Thaike—my friend Prince Golden Nest—approached me and said that the sawbwas present had unanimously voted to ask me to act as chief of all the hospitals supported by the states and responsible to them. I was to visit them once a month and continue to do surgery as I had been doing it under the British Military Administration; to train in surgery any doctors that could be spared; and to go all out in the training of nurses. For all this the states, he said, would collect an annual medical insurance fee of one rupee per house which they would place in a Central Medical Fund. From this Central Medical Fund they would pay for a new medical building in Namkham so the hospital there would be a fit place to train nurses; they would pay all expenses involved in training nurses; they would pay all expenses involved in my surgical tours; and they would pay me a salary of three thousand rupees a month. This last was a temptation because it might make possible a few improvements at Namkham.

While we were discussing the matter the British officer who was in charge of the administration of all the Frontier Areas arrived and asked me to extend the nurses' training to include a minimum of one hundred and twenty nurses who would be sent from the Chin Hills, Kachin State, Karenni State, and the Salween District as well as the Shan State. The Frontier Area Administration would pay for trainees even from the Shan States if the individual Shan states could not afford them.

These two propositions, taken together, were a bit overwhelming, since the little I had had of Government service had been too much. On the other hand they gave promise of fulfilling dreams I had always entertained—of reaching the less fortunate portions of Burma; of bringing together in the training school a greater variety of races even than before the war; of showing, as we had then, that you could really have a Union of Burma, where each race got along well and understood and enjoyed other races; and of continuing to take surgery into each state until all of the states believed in modern medical practice.

And as far as Government service was concerned, I had found no difficulty working with the sawbwas. As I saw it, I would now be a servant of the sick people, not the Government. The three big men in the Frontier Areas Administration were not difficult for me to get along with at all. And so I agreed to the proposition, provided Dr. Ba Saw or Dr. Gurney were allowed to alternate tours with me each month and also provided I was to be left with no bundles of red tape in running the work at Namkham.

A little later Colonel Lapping, a South African, was appointed Chief Medical Officer of the Frontier Areas. Sao Shwe Thaike called me aside and said they did not want Lapping, they wanted me. I pointed out to him that what they wanted me for was not the task of Chief Medical Officer. In such a job, I would be tied at a desk and would have no time for teaching or touring. Lapping was an extremely able man and an asset. What they wanted me for, I said, was as a consultant surgeon for their state hospitals, which the sawbwas themselves controlled. Finally Sao Shwe Thaike gave his approval.

Then Lapping came up with a scheme of medical development which was based on mine but was very much more elaborate. If I had been left alone, my scheme would have been effective in 1951 and Lapping's in 1961. But now the Government of Burma is developing a still more elaborate scheme of the same sort for all Burma as a part of their *Pyidawtha* program. Pyidawtha is supposed to be a translation of the words, "Welfare State." The Burmese express themselves much more poetically. The whole sentence, which is rubber-stamped on every paper, engraved on everything that will submit to engraving, included in every speech made on every subject, is *pyi-daw-tha-ya-me. Pyi-daw* is the Burmese way of saying the American "God's country," and the whole sentence, translated literally, is "God's country shall be pleasant." Not at all a bad star to hitch your wagon to, is it? If the effort progresses by the method of trial and error that is all the better. The miracle may not take place all at once, and some mistakes will certainly be made. But minor miracles are being accomplished all the time and when the big miracle comes—I do not say "if"—it will be in the true spirit of Burma, suitable to the needs of Burma and not taken *in toto* from some foreign country.

So we took on the jobs, and I drew pay for five months. This money was considered a buffer against the possible rainy day when first the individual Shan States and later the Government of the Frontier States should fail to pay their promised allotments on time. With the promise of the Frontier Areas Administration to pay for the training of nurses from states that could not afford to pay, girls came to us from areas that had never seen a nurse or doctor. In 1946 we had 210 girls, and by March, 1947, we had 260. It was the largest training school in Burma.

How on earth these girls were picked I have not the slightest idea. Most of them arrived without a word having been said to us in advance. Some eighty per cent were from good to excellent to most superior. Some ten per cent had nothing like the intelligence necessary for the study of nursing, and of these quite a few could not grasp even the one subject of midwifery. Half of the inherently able girls needed more education in our school before they could go all out in nurses' training. This was not a blow. This was one of the special services we desired to render to the country. And I have never seen as loyal or patriotic a group of teachers as those who served under our headmaster, Mr. Sein Hla Tha. They gave extra time to pre-nurses and even gave up their summer vacation to give special tutoring to the backward. But among these inherently able girls were some who had not yet reached adolescence, the youngest of all being sent by order of Colonel Lapping. For a time we looked like a kindergarten.

Lapping was most distressed by the medical needs of the Chin State and was determined to secure ten girls from that state at once. He took what girls he could get on three days' notice, and some of them must have come from villages without enough water to spare for bathing purposes. He drove them all to Namkham in his station wagon, one of those with a roof that folds back. When he arrived I was astonished to see four girls projecting out through the roof. It seemed an odd way to make girls travel, but when I shook hands with them I realized that Lapping was a very canny man in his disposition of these four girls. Ventilation was much better when his scheme was adopted.

But it was the last ten per cent of the original number of pupil nurses which really caused my hair to bristle. For the most part they were girls with brains—of the wrong kind. I know definitely how some of them happened to be sent to us: There was one state that bribed both the girls and their parents. Any girl who would come for nurses' training at Namkham was given six outfits of clothes—very scarce in those days—and her parents were given two hundred rupees as consolation for the temporary loss of their daughter. (Yet among the ten girls from this state two were very superior in every way.) In this last group were some girls who had kept the wolf from the door during the Japanese occupation by practicing the oldest profession. One had been rented by her father for a hundred rupees a month. They brought the wages of their profession with them in the form of diseases. One girl was a kleptomaniac. Several were sent by their parents because they did not want them around the house—they caused too much trouble. When we expelled four of them their fathers and mothers and brothers raised unmitigated Hades with us. They had put them in our school because they couldn't manage them, and thought we should have been able to do so; what were we for, anyway?

But these were a delight compared to those who were sent up by amateur politicians as agitators and informers. Now, our hospital and training school were absolutely wide open. Visitors were welcome at any time. We never censored letters received or sent by any of the girls. I had heartily approved when Taungbaing checked in advance to see whether we tried deliberately to destroy the Buddhist religion before he sent us the best he had. But when girls were sent to actually *keep* things in a turmoil—to exploit racial differences and personal differences among their companions, and to tear apart the work of the wards and classes —that was just a bit too much.

Eventually we had a total of twenty-eight different races, if you count the branches of Karens and Kachins and Chins who have different languages of their own as separate racial groups. Knowing that there would be many interracial problems, we had the nurses elect by ballot an interracial committee to advise us of any troubles that were threatening and to make suggestions as to the way to avoid them. Then, lest in ignorance of some Buddhist custom or festival we should commit an irremediable *faux pas*, we had the Buddhist girls select members by states for a Buddhist committee.

Both of these committees were of tremendous significance. Each of them not only accomplished assigned tasks but would assemble when some very great moral or morale difficulty arose: when some girl, for example, was, on her own initiative, destroying the character of the nurses or the prestige of the school. Save in a case when a girl failed in all her work, no girl was expelled without the consent—or the demand—of these committees.

Later when the political uprisings in Burma became a problem there was a risk that blame would attach to the nurses if they gave us their advice in this democratic manner. Then it became necessary for me, after asking informal advice, to make the final decisions myself and to assume full responsibility for everything that was done. Had I not done so a lot of poor innocents could have been dragged into trouble during my imprisonment. This gave rise, I think, to the later statement that I was dictatorial and overbearing in the way I ran Namkham. People who know the truth know better. Namkham was run very democratically. But when there is trouble in the offing it hardly behooves the boss of an institution to hide behind the girls' *longyis,* and the few men on our staff just weren't taking any responsibility. If a scapegoat must be sacrificed it should be the top goat.

But none of these troubles appeared in 1946. The agitators were not sent until early 1947 and did not get really organized until early 1948. In 1946 and 1947, teaching these nurses was a sheer delight.

Our surgical tours under the new setup were successful from the start. We split up the group of our war-service girls and put them in little hospitals where there were no doctors. All these were in the Southern Shan States or in Karenni. It was British policy that caused this; the situation was an anomaly. The Northern States were then five in number, all of them great states, although Taungbaing at the time was bankrupt. Since prewar days their sawbwas had had plenty of pull and had accordingly been supplied with doctors by the medical department of the Government of Burma. At the end of the Japanese occupation the civil government was willing to place doctors only where there had been doctors in prewar days. Thus the Northern States got their doctors.

With our medical scheme, the states that were lucky enough to get our wartime nurses prospered. Yawngwhe State especially prospered, for their original doctor was ex-

pelled by the sawbwa and a Punjabi doctor named Ghei
was placed there. Dr. Ghei was exceptional. He had served
all over Burma with distinction and he deserved the
Yawngwhe berth. He had two Namkham nurses under him.
Taunggyi, Kalaw, Loilem, Kutkai, and Lashio all had civil or
military posts, and their hospitals were directly under the
Government of Burma. These, therefore, were crossed off
my list. Kutkai and Lashio did not matter; their major
surgery usually went to Namkham anyway. Loilem went to
Gurney at Panglong. Occasional cases from Kalaw came
to me in Aungban. Taunggyi and all the Inle Lake area
went to Yawngwhe.

Dr. Gurney, who was rapidly rebuilding the hospital and
the prewar Anglican mission work in Panglong, alternated
with me on visits to Yawngwhe. From my very first visit
there I was overwhelmed by the number of patients who
required careful physical examination in consultation with
Drs. Goswami and Ghei, and I remember we never had less
than fifteen operations a day, most of them very difficult.
After two or three visits I sent for Dr. Ghei.

"Doctor, why on earth are there always so many patients
here?"

"That's easy. As soon as Sao Shwe Thaike learns the day
of your intended visit he sends the town crier with his gong
to all the bazaars and notifies the people that the Old American Doctor will be here tomorrow."

"So that is what they call me, is it? How do they an-
nounce Dr. Gurney? As the English Doctor?"

"No, indeed; Dr. Gurney—well, he is the *Young* American Doctor."

I don't believe Dr. Gurney will ever live that one down.

While I had been serving under the British Military Administration I had had as an associate a young Burmese doctor named Ba Win. He had been a lecturer in anatomy at the University of Rangoon for seven years before the war, and in that time had forgotten much of his medicine. But during the war years he had taken refuge in Nampan, which is the third largest bazaar town in the Shan States, located at the southern end of Inle Lake. Because of his unstinted efforts in their behalf the Inthas at Nampan had become most attached to him and wanted him back as soon as the Civil Government took over. But Ba Win had intelligence enough to realize he had forgotten his surgery and medicine, so he asked the sawbwa for permission to study at Namkham. Sao Shwe Thaike agreed, and Nampan approved. So Ba Win came to Namkham, where he stayed for nearly a year. With his excellent knowledge of anatomy he took to surgery like an American does to gadgets. He also took to Little Bawk, the Kachin nurse of war days who was a natural at surgery, eloped with her, and the two of them, on returning to Nampan, soon had a most thriving hospital, although their only building was a corrugated iron oven in the bazaar. From the time I first visited them, Nampan had as many operative cases waiting as the town of Yawngwhe.

Yawngwhe received more benefit from our surgery than any other state and wore me out more than any state except Kengtung, which was so hard to reach. On our arrival at the town of Yawngwhe, we would report to Dr. Ghei so he would be able to send word to distant places that I had actually arrived and that operations would begin at a certain time. Then we would climb into an outboard motorboat, bag and baggage, sterile supplies and surgical instruments, and set off for Nampan. At Nampan, while giving the patients time to gather, there was always a chance of stowing away a dozen or two of the most delicious bananas in the world, the Shan perfume-bananas. Bawk and Ba Win knew my weaknesses and catered to them.

Nampan patients were always from nearby villages, whereas Yawngwhe patients were sometimes from as far away as Meiktila and Myingyan in Burma Proper. Therefore it was essential for me to be at Yawngwhe to begin operations at the hour set, and thereafter Nampan had to take what was left of me. Operations would begin at Nampan at any time of the day or night, depending on how many cases there were. On one trip we began at ten at night, continued until half-past two in the morning, slept till six, and then began again. Never in my life have I suffered so from mosquitoes as I have while operating at Nampan. The white-papered walls of the operating room were black with them.

The Ba Wins live in a bamboo house built up on very high bamboo stilts in water five feet deep. The fish took care of all necessary sanitary arrangements. The only trouble with me was that I was finicky; I never bathed in Nampan and never ate fish there. Under Ba Win's house was a floating island on which they grew bananas and raised chickens, lots of puppies, and even one small pig. They had gone out in a dugout onto the lake until they found a floating island that suited their purposes, had taken a hitch onto it and towed back to their home, where they moored it.

In each of the hospitals for which graduate-nurse midwives could not be obtained, a senior and a junior nurse were stationed for two months' rotation duty. We staggered the girls, taking out one new girl for each hospital on our monthly trips. Thus there was always one girl who had been there for a month, who knew what patients were being treated from the previous month. This service went on without interruption.

It was a great scheme. The girls were away from formal training at Namkham for not more than two months at a time, and during this absence learned unforgettable lessons in self-reliance, responsibility, and tact towards patients and rulers, as well as in geography and a spirit of oneness with other races. Always one of the girls was chosen for her ability to speak the language of the area. The others were purposely mixed up. Kachins and Karens served Shan areas, Karens and Shans served Kachin areas. Some girls went so far as to acquire the new language during their period of outside duty, which was something few of them ever bothered to do at Namkham, where they could always make a companion talk strange languages for them. It is regrettable that the rebellions later made it impossible to continue this work, for thousands of sick had thus been able to obtain medical care, while these nurses received the best training that we have ever been able to give.

As soon as we placed nurses at Samka, halfway to Loikaw, we had to visit the river Bilu Chaung, using the motorboat we had taken to Nampan. This is a most interesting river. It is the outlet of Inle Lake, and the only way of reaching the beautiful country through which it flows; a few miles south of Loikaw, it suddenly disappears into the earth. Twice on the Bilu Chaung, attacks on villages by armed robbers occurred just before or just after we had passed. Attacks of this sort also occurred when we were traveling by car to other hospitals. While these bandits would attack other people, they always left our hospital car or boat alone.

Water hyacinths make the entrance to the Bilu Chaung from the lake as obscure as the entrance to the lake from Yawngwhe. Our motorboat captain was lost several times before he finally found the open stream. His devious course let us see the way the Inthas had reaped their rice out of water and had hung it up to dry on bamboo poles. I have still not discovered how people who live in a lake thrash or winnow rice, but the way the Inthas do it must be good.

The open river flowed swiftly by great open meadows which made me positively homesick for Ohio. Where it narrowed there were trees along the shore, on each of which hung as many as a dozen nests of the weaver bird, with their openings in the bottom, leading to a little waterproof compartment in the top for the mother bird and the eggs. Then came rapids, where everyone prayed the engine would not die at the wrong time. There were villages with the largest and most beautiful Buddhist monasteries I think I have ever seen.

From the river you land on some uninhabited bank and walk half a mile to Samka town, invariably missing the road to the hospital and having to beg someone to escort you back.

On one trip we did a goiter operation on the floor, since there were no boxes or combination of tables that we could use. And there was that niece of the sawbwa, who wanted me to bore her ears for little diamond-studded soft-gold pins. As soon as the operations were finished we started back. The senior nurse was a Shan who was already quite at home in Samka, so she did not bother to come to the river to see us off. But the young nurse named Peggy, whom we had brought, had never been left in a strange place before. Broken-hearted at the thought of being left behind, she went on ahead to the river and stowed herself away behind our pile of luggage. The other girls found her, of course, and she had to climb out. Then she grabbed hold of my hand and stood smiling with the tears streaming out of her eyes while trying to keep the boat from moving away, with the other nurses laughing at her. Even if I had known how much trouble this young Peggy was going to cause me a year later with her boy friends and her tale-bearing and her rumor-mongering and her elopement with the Karen rebels, I still would have been touched at the sight of that girl trying to cover her flowing tears with a smile. Perhaps if I had known more psychology and psychiatry I could have saved this pitiful girl from herself, and I still have a poignant feeling of regret when I remember her.

Just about this time we posted an absolutely charming Karen girl named Stella to a tiny hospital not far from a big Government hospital. Stella was one of nine super-superior nurses in training. There was one more Karen and the others were Kachin, Shan, and one Mon. When Stella was sent to see one very ill patient, she discovered that he had plague. She ordered the family to get the Government doctor at once. The doctor came, said the case was hopeless and left. The family came back to Stella and begged that she do something, no matter what. Remembering that in my lectures on bubonic plague I had stated that with a disease like plague *any* treatment was legitimate and that especial attention should be given to the use of antibiotics and the more powerful sulfa drugs, Stella hunted through her stores, found a bottle of sodium-sulfadiazine that she had purloined from Namkham. She gave it intravenously. The patient turned the corner and eventually got well.

A year later Stella, who had developed tuberculosis from overwork, was traveling in a jeep to her home in Taunggyi for a month or two of recuperation. Her jeep ran into Government troops who arrested her on suspicion of her being a rebel and she was thrown into jail for fourteen months. That Stella came out of jail alive and sane proves God has a big task waiting for her which no lesser person can handle. All her clothes and personal belongings were removed in Lashio, and she was living in borrowed rags when I saw her on my release from prison. When I gave her two hundred rupees to refit herself with decent clothing she broke down and sobbed. She has recently finished her training in the Mission Hospital in Moulmein.

7

Our "Union of Burma"

BY THE early fall of 1946 Namkham had completely recovered, the hospital and nurses' training school were in the top of their form, and our surgical tours left little to be desired, so in October I set out for a lecture tour of six months in the United States.

When I had come back to America in 1945 it had been as an army officer to a country at war. This time the feeling was different. I was an American returning home. Our plane touched down at the Boston Airport. Undoubtedly it was a silly thing to do, but when I got down from that plane I walked away from the crowd, picked up a handful of good old American earth and let it sift through my fingers.

I was born in Burma, but my first childhood memory is of America, to which the family had taken me on their furlough when I was three years old. It had been so long since they had last been in the States that the American relatives had all moved West. It was natural, then, that in selecting a spot for their furlough the family should have chosen Hamilton, New York, where so many of them had taken their college work in Madison University. Whether Hamilton always has such very wintry winters I cannot say, but apparently that year the snow had deeply covered the ground for months. My first childhood memory is of the spring thaws uncovering the long-forgotten autumn leaves of the previous fall and of the spring flowers then pushing up in all their fresh beauty. A trifling thing for a first memory? Hardly. Spring in America is never trifling to any self-exiled American.

I am not a man without a country. I am a man with two countries, both of which are home, and to both of which I feel a profound loyalty. It is true that fewer years of my life have been spent in America than in Burma, but when I am home in the States I take very large, concentrated doses of America. These doses are large enough not only to satisfy my accrued hunger but sufficient also to get me well started on another few years of voluntary absence. When I am in America I talk to everyone about Burma; when I am in Burma I talk to everyone about America. In my heart the two countries are inseparable.

Now, as any good doctor will tell you, it is necessary for him to spend a month each year or three months every three years to take refresher courses under someone who is bigger than he is. If he does not do so he is soon out of date, no matter how many medical magazines he takes and reads. And so it is with America. No matter how many American magazines and books a self-exiled American may buy and study, he still needs to go back to the States every so often and take a refresher course in America. That is what I was doing in the fall and winter of 1946–1947. I was visiting with my wife and children, I was giving lectures on Burma, and I was taking a refresher course in America.

On my return to Namkham in the spring of 1947 I threw my hat in a corner, picked up a team, and started right out on a surgical tour with Kengtung as the first stop. Then for three days, as we traveled, I cursed myself for setting out when nobody expected me back in Burma for two more weeks; thereby I was making it impossible for patients to be ready for me in Kengtung. So I projected myself ahead of the car and willed the doctor at Kengtung to know that I was on my way, that I would arrive at a certain time, and that he should have patients ready for me. And when I got there the doctor merely said hello unconcernedly, told me arrangements had been made for me to sleep at a certain Paya Lai's house, and that he was giving a dinner for me at his home in a couple of hours.

"What about operations?"

"There are six waiting in the hospital. I sent for two others three days ago and they should arrive tonight."

"How did you know I was coming?"

"I just knew, that's all."

Money was already becoming scant, and the Central Fund was paying me no more as salary. I didn't want the money for myself, but I did want it as a buffer between us and want. In several of the state hospitals served by our nurses we had to advance thousands of rupees to keep the hospitals going until the state treasuries paid for the medicines and the nurses' expenses. But the nurses' training school was doing well and was the largest in Burma. Dr. Ba Saw and Dr. Tu were so expert and had such a profound influence in North Burma that the average number of beds filled had actually gone up since my departure. The new medical building had been completed, dedicated, and was in use. A lot of complicated cases had been saved for me. A period of only six months loomed ahead for me to catch up on my work and get ahead in the teaching. Then I would have to leave again to fulfill my contract for one more lecture tour in America.

Our policy towards the Buddhist girls was beginning to pay off well. Buddhist girls came to Christian ceremonies and Christian girls went to Buddhist ceremonies. One Intha girl from Yawngwhe named Nyunt Tin, who was a very sincere Buddhist, used to gather Christian girls around her and explain her beliefs. The Christian girls told me how much they enjoyed her expositions and how they were beginning to appreciate the Buddhist point of view. I discovered that certain girls had adopted as best friends girls of other races. And invariably these girls were in the group who were superior in hospital and classroom work when the staff listed that group for me. I was especially pleased by the friendship which had sprung up between Buddhist-Shan Alice San Tip from Kengtung and Christian-Kachin Ah Tawt from Myitkyina, the girl whose legs had been fractured at Kutkai. This friendship began and continued in the face of considerable criticism from Christians and Buddhists, from Shans and Kachins. In spite of these cracks, however, the other girls looked up to both Alice and Ah Tawt with sincere respect.

Frequently we asked the girls to put on entertainments. Each class had to produce something, and so did each racial group. When the racial groups produced their own tribal dances in costume they drew the most applause, though everyone loved it when the Intha girls dressed up as boys and girls and put on a satire of a modern Burmese play. These entertainments had girls of one race clapping harder for girls of another race than they did for their own. While I had been away President-elect Sao Shwe Thaike had made a tour of Burma and had visited Namkham. My sister Grace asked the girls to put on one of these entertainments for him; at the close he sighed:

"You certainly have a Union of Burma here."

We had had a Union of Burma at Namkham for fifteen years, I thought, before anyone in Burma Proper had even considered the matter.

Two surgical tours were especially memorable. On one I had only two nurses, the Christian Kachin and Buddhist Shan who were fast friends. At the beginning of the trip we were talking to the sawbwa when I was called into one of the bedrooms to examine a woman who was ill. On a table in the corner was the cradle used by the prospective crown prince of each generation. It was of silver, about four feet by two, and fifteen inches high. Studded into the sides in V's were probably two hundred matched sapphires from Mogok, and at the points of these V's there were matched rubies. I nearly fainted, and the girls were furious with me because they had not been called in to see it.

But their reaction wasn't quite fair, for in most places no sooner had the jeep stopped than my time was occupied with the sawbwa on business related to the hospital, while the girls invariably took off for the harem and got themselves posted on all the latest gossip. In one state five hundred miles away from the one just mentioned they came out goggle-eyed. They had just seen the duplicate cradle of the other, only this one was of gold.

We came to a third state where the sawbwa was unfriendly, so I suggested that the girls remain in the jeep. When I had first met this sawbwa he had sixteen wives. Six weeks later a military-government friend visited him and he had twenty-two. How many he had at this point, I didn't know. He was probably trying to imitate one of the last sultans of Turkey, who married a new wife every Friday. He certainly was way behind the famous gentleman of Baghdad whom Scheherazade tamed.

The sawbwa's palace was one which had been completely demolished by bombs, so he was living in temporary quarters of bamboo and thatch, consisting of a big central building entirely surrounded by at least twenty dovecotes about sixteen feet square. As I walked up only the sawbwa and his mahadevi were visible. The sawbwa and I went into the huge parlor and talked business for half an hour and then I left. When I climbed back into the jeep the girls were bursting with news. They could scarcely wait until we had passed out of earshot.

"You know, the minute you disappeared inside, the heads of beautiful girls stuck out of every window of those things you called dovecotes, and they just stared until they saw you start to come out. Then they all popped back in again!"

On that trip, with only two girls, we made the circuit of the small states in the southwest border area. One stop was at Pindaya, which I consider one of the most beautiful spots in the world. Around a bend in the road there spreads out in front of you a beautiful blue lake with a backdrop of high mountains. On those mountains are hundreds of small white pagodas built along stone steps which lead up to the mouth of a huge cave. This cave is a holy place to the Buddhists. Inside are very sacred images of the Buddha, and there is even a full-size pagoda built within the cave itself. I turned to the Buddhist girl, whose name was Hkam Mai.

"Wouldn't you like to take time out to visit the cave, worship there, and acquire a lot of merit?"

"Oh, Daddy! Could I?"

So we walked up those awful steps to the mouth of the cave. I took off my shoes, for this was sacred ground, and we walked through the cave while the Shan girl worshiped to her heart's content.

When we returned to Taunggyi there was a telegram waiting for me, asking me to come at once to Rangoon.

"Well, girls, you're lucky. Hkam Mai can now get a lot of merit worshiping at the Shwe Dagon Pagoda."

As we were going through Pegu I suddenly turned off the highway on a dirt road leading to the right.

"Now, where do you think you're going?" asked the Kachin girl.

"What? You don't mean to tell me you girls don't know about the enormous reclining image of Buddha here in Pegu? Surely you want to worship there, Hkam Mai?"

Hkam Mai's eyes sparkled. But just as we reached the image a large nail punctured one of my tires. So while the girls were in the shrine and Hkam Mai was acquiring merit by leaps and bounds, I was out in the hot sun changing the tire and thinking such mean thoughts that all the merit I might have acquired in a lifetime was oozing out of my pores as fast as Hkam Mai was absorbing it.

The other trip was when I received word that my new De Soto, the gift of a friend in the United States, had reached Rangoon. Deciding to combine two tasks, we started a surgical tour to Loikaw and then took the road through the Karenni States and the Mawchi Mines to Toungoo and on down. My jeep was almost worn out, and on our way to Mawchi the road was so full of nails from bombed-out buildings that we had puncture after puncture —about one in every two miles. By the time we arrived at Mawchi it was already dark. There were the everlasting gates where we stopped for identification before losing our way several times in the town. I knew no one at Mawchi then and didn't want to stop to sleep till we had reached a village about thirty-five miles farther on where we had an acquaintance.

We stopped for identification at one or two more gates the other side of Mawchi. Then, high in the mountains and in dense jungle, I saw the bright lights of a bus coming downhill about a mile off. I had the right of way, but you don't argue things like that on a one-way road. So I stopped for about ten minutes and waited for the bus to appear. Nothing happened, and I thought the driver was following the rules and waiting for me. So I drove on. The bus was parked at a wide corner. Just as I drew abreast a man ran out from behind the bus and signaled to me to stop. He was not in uniform. I just stepped on the gas, wondering when the bullet would hit me. For this was the day of marauding gangs of bandits, and stopping on the order of a man in civvies in the middle of dense jungle is something one did not do, especially at night. The road was so bad that it was midnight before we reached our friend's house and had a meal of cold rice.

We were off at dawn. As we crossed the great Sittang bridge on the edge of Toungoo an armed policeman stepped into the middle of the bridge at the far end and signaled to me to stop.

"When did you pass Mawchi?"

"Last night about dusk."

"Then this telegram must be about you."

The telegram informed the authorities at Toungoo:

UNIDENTIFIED JEEP ASSUMED TO BE CARRYING
CONTRABAND OPIUM PASSED THROUGH MAWCHI SEVEN
P.M. AND REFUSED STOP GATES. PLEASE ARREST
ON ARRIVAL.

The policeman climbed on the side of the jeep next to me so he could interfere if I pulled any funny business, and we drove to the police station. I walked in and sat down; I had a long wait before the Police Superintendent would see me. He was an Anglo-Burman; he didn't like my looks even after he had looked me over carefully.

"Why didn't you stop at the gates?"

"I did stop at every gate and was passed on recognition. The only place I refused to stop was when a man in civilian clothes ran out from behind a bus in the jungle fifteen miles this side of Mawchi. I certainly didn't stop for him."

"We will have to search your jeep."

"Search it from top to bottom, all you like."

"Who are you, anyway?"

I handed over my passport and driver's license.

"Are you Doctor Seagrave of Namkham?"

"Can't deny it."

"If you are Doctor Seagrave you can carry all the contraband you want, for all I care. You operated on my wife before the war. Next case!"

I was gratified at the trust in me thus expressed. I would have been even more so if I could have foreseen how events would change all that.

When we drew up in front of the old house in Rangoon

my poor old jeep let out one last sigh and gave up the
ghost. The De Soto was grand, and we finished our surgical
tour in real style. The only trouble with the De Soto was
that it was too long for some corners. Also it was slung so
low that the great rocks that truck drivers use to prop up
their wheels while they clean out their carburetors, and then
invariably leave in the middle of the road, were a menace.

Nurses East and West

THERE is one joy in this world that can be equaled by no other pleasure with which I am acquainted. That is the satisfaction of having too much work to do and then going ahead and getting it done anyway. With all my different jobs there had to be a plan to make my work effective. As far as nurses' training was concerned the thing I could do better than anyone else was explaining new subjects. Sister Grace and the top nurses were much better at drilling the girls and in conducting recitations. When I was in Namkham, therefore, I lectured extra hours, day after day, until the pupil-nurses' brains were saturated with new material. Then when I went on tour Grace and the matrons split up my subjects and reviewed them, drilling the girls until they were letter-perfect and ready for another heavy meal on my return.

In the wards I took no regular work. Grace kept control of the obstetrical and pediatrics wards, because none of our doctors had proceeded quite far enough in these subjects to compare with her. Moreover, they were too busy learning surgery, which is what most doctors pine for when they come to Namkham for training. At Namkham as well as in the entire Shan State I was definitely only the consultant. The younger doctors split up all the other wards.

Dr. Ba Saw was the immediate consultant on matters surgical and Dr. Tu on matters medical. Whenever they were unsure they would call me in, and we would argue the case together.

On Sunday mornings the doctors and staff nurses went on rounds of the entire hospital with me. This gave our younger doctors the chance they loved most of all. In Burma doctors are avid readers of any medical book, and at Namkham they had access to new American books and magazines as well as their own English textbooks. They would read up everything in sight and then on these Sunday mornings they would ask me the most abstruse, insane, or pointless questions based upon some obscure paragraph in a more obscure book. The whole purpose of asking me the question was not to obtain information—they had already read up what information there was in the book. The game was to force me to say, in front of the entire staff, especially the good-looking nursing staff, that I didn't know what the answer was. They got so much pleasure out of showing me up that I proceeded to get still more perverse pleasure out of showing myself up and calling the attention of the pupil-nurses to the fact that Doctor So-and-so had asked me such a profound question that I was entirely unable to reply. I doubt if anyone got the point except our two matrons, E Hla and Naomi, and sometimes Emily, if she had time to join us on rounds, and they would turn to each other and grin. A Shan, a Taungthu and an Indo-Burman—the sense of humor of the women in Burma is a heartwarming thing.

Unless some terrible emergency came in I did my surgical work only on Saturdays. On the other days of the week the younger doctors did the ordinary surgery, with either Dr. Tu or Dr. Ba Saw scrubbed up and helping them. More difficult surgery was done by Dr. Tu, with Dr. Ba Saw scrubbing up and assisting him. Cases a step worse than that, Dr. Ba Saw handled himself. The really complicated things were left for Saturdays or were saved up during the weeks I was on tour and then the three of us would go to town. Frequently we had three operating tables in use at the same time. Once, while I was doing a gynecological operation with Dr. Ba Saw, Dr. Tu, busy with a goiter, let out a wail of anguish as his hemostat slipped off the superior thyroid artery. I had him shove his thumb in there while I doffed my gloves and gown, donned others, and then showed him how to get that hemorrhage under control.

Dr. Ba Saw, though he made no complaints, had some doubts about my method of teaching by practical example. But he completely changed his views after he had been in Louisville, Kentucky—where they made him "learn by doing," just as I did. I know about a hundred young doctors in Burma who would give several years of their lives to be able to "learn by doing" with an older doctor to take the responsibility for the patient's life off their shoulders. That is the trouble with surgery in Burma. The surgeon makes so much money that he does the operations himself and won't teach the men under him anything, if he can possibly help it. This dates way back to British times. I know a superb English surgeon who left Burma practically a millionaire. Not one of his pupils can do the surgery he used to do; he never gave them a chance to learn.

All the really abandoned cases we had at Namkham came from a long distance, from the farther reaches of the Kachin State or from Burma Proper. Carcinomata and sarcomata were much more common than in prewar days. There was only one variety of case that I really resented—women with

all their pelvic organs messed up by penicillin-fast gonorrhea. The research men develop a drug as marvelous as
penicillin—and then doctors misuse it. It would not have
been misused if our first penicillin in Burma had been one
of the varieties which require only one dose a day. But the
only penicillin we had from 1945 to 1947 was either out-
dated green penicillin or ordinary penicillin sodium. Doctors
then simply would not give injections every three hours
themselves—except Phyllis Krasu, who used her alarm clock
and nearly killed herself doing it—nor would they allow
nurses to give the injections for them. The result was one
injection a day or one a week or whenever the patient happened to turn up, and then the country was swept with
penicillin-fast gonorrhea that nothing but the knife will
cure.

Our experience at Namkham is that everything happens
by threes. Our first ruptured gastric ulcer of postwar times
had been put back to bed after the operation only a few
hours when our second came in from exactly the opposite
direction, promptly followed by a third who had come all
the way from Namtu to perforate his ulcer at nearby Muse.
The big exception to this rule was our first postwar extra-
uterine pregnancies. One of our old girls was brought in by
truck from Kutkai, where her extra-uterine pregnancy had
ruptured five or six hours previously. I was astounded to have
her alive, only to be still more astounded when, the next
morning, *another* graduate nurse was carried in on a stretcher
with a typical history of ruptured extra-uterine pregnancy,
her rupture having taken place two days earlier. She was
white-lipped on arrival, and I was sure she would not live,
but with two bottles of ex-U. S. Army plasma we pulled
her through the worst of the shock and operated on her.

And then our eyes really did pop. She had had twin pregnancies, one in each tube, and both were ruptured. And still she could not die. She is back at full-time nursing now, running her own small hospital and supporting a completely useless husband.

With a schedule like this one cannot afford to be sick. Yet where many operations are done at night or in strange places, one cannot avoid ameba-carrying flies and malaria mosquitoes. For dysentery I used a large dose of chlorodyne to force my large intestine to stay quiet until the operation or lecture was over. For malaria a hot-water bag held in place at the small of my back by a bandage, plus a blanket or two wrapped around the lower half of my body, used to help a lot. On one trip at Mong Kung the chill began just as I started operating, and by the time I finished my temperature was 104! While the nurses cleaned up and repacked I sweated it off, and then we drove on. The chief difficulty when I am lecturing under the influence of malaria or dysentery is to introduce the right amount of humor into my lectures so the nurses won't go to sleep. When I am sick I seem to forget my best jokes.

Then October, 1947, came around, and I had to fly back to the States for my second lecture tour. One of our big trucks followed me as I drove down to Rangoon in the De Soto after doing surgery in the most important states. When we reached Tatkon I noticed a big sign by the police station.

"Road unsafe due to Communists. Cars may pass only in convoy."

I drove into the station.

"When does your next convoy leave?"

"Tomorrow morning at ten."

"Does that sign mean you are going to stop me if I start through?"

"If you go, you go at your own risk."

I cannot remember ever having traveled at anyone's risk other than my own, so we drove on. But long before we reached Pyinmana we came to a half-mile of mudholes, and even the big truck got stuck. The men slept on the ground, the women in the truck, and I in the De Soto. In the morning a lot of Burmese came down to look us over. They seemed to like the looks of the American digging away hopelessly at mud, for they turned to and soon pulled us out. Whether they were Communists or not I never heard.

After I had arrived in the States, in the latter half of November, the four nurses who were coming over for postgraduate study were due to dock in Boston. I was worried: These girls had never been out of the tropics, and they had nothing to wear but thin *longyis* and *aingyis* and an occasional light sweater. Now, Boston in November is a very windy city. I was so worried that my friends in New York gathered together four of the warmest and smallest overcoats they could find. Fortified with these, I took the train to Boston and there, thick overcoat and all, I almost froze to death waiting for the ship to dock. The girls came running down the gangplank and then suddenly stopped and gaped at the four overcoats.

"There, I told you so," came the voice of a lady behind them, and the girls blushed.

I was so excited at the girls' arrival that I got all their baggage and themselves into two taxis but completely forgot my own two bags parked in a warm customs office. It was not until we were finishing a hurried lunch in South Station and had five minutes to catch our train that I remembered my own bags and had to send back from New York for them.

"Now, come on and tell me what that American lady was talking about at the dock," I ordered, as we relaxed in the day coach.

"Oh, Daddy," they cried—they were so full of their experiences that they all talked at once, chattering along in Burmese. One girl would begin a sentence, another would snatch the words out of her mouth, and a third would finish, while the fourth was ready to start the next sentence.

"Everyone was so good to us on the steamer, and we stopped in Genoa and we never saw destitute, starving white people before, and the children were just pitiful. Do you know, they came and rummaged in our garbage! . . . Yes, and I threw down an apple . . . and I gave a *longyi* to a poor old woman in rags. And the sailors taught us how to fish over the side in the Red Sea and just as we were getting into Djibouti Pansy got a bite . . . and the fish was so gigantic it nearly jerked me over the side. And the Captain gave a dinner . . . yes, and our two best American girl friends dressed up in Burmese clothes . . . and they dressed us up in American evening dresses . . . yes, and Pansy nearly fell out of the top of her dress . . . but Ruby looked swell in hers. And Esther and Hla Sein and Pansy were seasick all the way to Ceylon . . . well, you needn't brag, you froze all the way across the Atlantic!"

"Yes, yes," I said. "But you haven't told me yet about that cryptic remark at the dock."

"Well, we told everyone when we boarded the ship at Calcutta . . . that we were some of Dr. Seagrave's nurses.

And then it was so cold on the Atlantic . . . and all I had was a light sweater . . . my little Namkham short coat didn't do me a bit of good . . . and they kept scaring us about how much colder it was in Boston. . . ."

"But what has this to do with the American lady?"

"Well," said all four together for once, "she said she bet you would be at the dock with four long coats hanging on your arm, and then we saw the four coats before we saw you!"

. Squiring four Burman girls around New York is quite an undertaking. Four blocks from our hotel was an Automat, which I was sure would appeal to them, but I hardly realized how fascinated they would be by it. At first they were frightened and didn't turn the knobs hard enough when they put in their nickels. Then Ruby put one nickel too many in a slot. She thought the nickel was lost for good and could not believe her eyes when her extra nickel came rolling back to her. Then they had an attack of worrying how much the nickel was worth in Burmese money, and there was a short-lived epidemic of trying to eat almost nothing. But they soon succumbed to the fascination of it and were eating twice as much, I swear, as they would have eaten in an ordinary restaurant. They were so overcome by the way the cream and coffee came separately out of the spout and never overflowed their cups that they drank twice as much coffee as was good for them.

But in the streets it was awful. Esther and Pansy consented to be led, but Hla Sein and Ruby walked with necks twisted so they could gaze up at the towering skyscrapers, entirely oblivious of traffic. Hla Sein had a penchant for bumping into hurrying Americans on the sidewalks. Ruby would ignore the red lights and wander out into the middle of a street, still stargazing, while truck drivers tore their hair in anguish.

Two very charming ladies took us all shopping at Macy's and Gimbel's so they could advise the girls on what clothes to buy. The girls had more sense than to stop wearing Burmese *aingyis* and *longyis*, but they needed really good shoes and stockings and warm coats.

When we finished shopping it was pouring rain. Thinking we might find a taxi at the Pennsylvania Station, the ladies took us down into the subway and along the underground tunnel. In the press of the crowd a hand jerked my sleeve.

"Do you suppose those are some of Dr. Seagrave's Burmese nurses?" asked a pleasant woman.

"Yes, Ma'am, they are—I am Dr. Seagrave, and this is Esther, whose picture is in *Burma Surgeon*."

One good friend had given us seats for *Oklahoma!* Since all four girls were Karens I knew they would love the music, but I thought they might miss some of the jokes and insinuations in the lyrics, especially in "Ev'rythin's Up To Date in Kansas City," "I Cain't Say No," and "All er Nuthin'." They didn't miss a thing. In fact, I had to hold onto them to keep them from rolling down the aisle with laughter.

Some ladies invited the four girls to tea, and they went in fear and trembling. They had grown used to American men during the war, but they were still uncertain of American women in spite of the kindness shown to them on their first shopping excursion. When the girls returned from the tea their faces were glowing. They had again been treated as attractive equals with a gracious spontaneity which Americans know so well how to use when they choose. There had been no condescension shown.

Then NBC found out about the girls, and they had to go to Rockefeller Center where the express elevators astonished, terrified, and even sickened them until they learned not to resist the pull and drop. While Mary Margaret McBride interviewed them the television man was listening in, and later they appeared on television, too. I was relieved when at long last Hla Sein and Ruby secured their nursing costumes and started work in Jersey City's Margaret Hague Hospital and Esther and Pansy were safely settled with the Louisville Board of Health.

9

The Strike

IN LATE July, 1948, I was asked by U Nu (Thakin Nu) to come to Rangoon and sit on a commission to study the mortality rate in Burma of women and children, which was the highest rate in the world since World War II. Although I had met him in 1946, this was my first chance to study U Nu. He is a very handsome man of medium Burmese height, and an ideal exponent of "How To Win Friends and Influence People"—which, incidentally, he has translated into Burmese. Although I was just an old American doctor who was spending his life in the wilder and more remote areas of Burma, he was very gracious to me on my visit in 1948 and took time from his busy life to exert his full charm of manner. And when U Nu desires to be charming he can be very charming indeed. His English is superb. To me, in fact, his English is even more appealing than his Burmese speeches, in which his imagery is distinctly Burmese in character and idiom, so therefore does not make a good impression when translated literally into English, as has so often been the case when reporters quote him in the newspapers. To enjoy one of U Nu's Burmese speeches a foreigner must stop thinking in his own language and think in Burmese, and thus absorb U Nu's language without translation. I tried that once when I was sitting

almost at his feet, and it was very effective. The translation
I read later was a crude reflection of what he had really said.

After this pleasant meeting with U Nu, life was calm for
a brief time. Then came a grievous disturbance. It was on
September 4, 1948, that we had our great nurses' strike.

I shall now have to go back a bit for the background.
When this Frontier Areas Nurses' Training School was
started, there was great poverty in the Frontier States. Because of this, when I was asked to specify the amount of
money which would be needed to support a pupil-nurse per
month I had followed my prewar plan. I asked for the
absolute minimum which would be necessary to keep a
girl decently and give her a good but not elaborate diet.
Then three things happened. First, the cost of everything
went up, so much so that Emily, who had had a special
course in diet and housekeeping, found it all but impossible
to keep her budget for food out of the red; then, the Government of the Union of Burma advertised in all the newspapers
for pupil-nurses for their own training schools, offering to
spend some three times as much for each student as we were
allowed to spend. When I suggested increases in our grants
they were refused. And finally, trouble-makers were sent in
to distribute gripes wholesale. These four trouble-makers
among the nurses were real *agents provocateurs*—tools of
petty politicians who wanted them in our ranks to under-
mine our unity and my authority and generally to show
who was boss. Of course, these agents made great ammunition out of the larger grants offered by the Government, for
the nurses knew nothing of my appeals in their behalf.

Some of the nurses started stealing food from the storerooms and from each other. This was not universal; it was

confined only to the girls who ought never to have been in training. But it worked a very real hardship on the decent, hardworking girls. The only person Emily could trust to guard the pantry was my orderly of World War II days, Pang Tze. He and Emily kept the keys.

Now we come to the incident that started the strike.

I had finished teaching a class at about four in the afternoon. In this class was a fine Hkamti girl from the northern tip of Burma, near the snow mountains. After her class left, I had one more lecture to give and was about halfway through this last lecture when this Hkamti girl came running to me, sobbing hysterically and quite incoherent. All I could make out was that something terrible had occurred in the nurses' mess hall. I patted her on the back, quieted her a bit, and asked her to stick around outside for fifteen minutes till I could finish my lecture, and then I would go into the matter. As soon as I could, I called her in and learned that she had been in the storeroom looking for the regular evening meal before the whistle blew. Pang Tze had assumed she was in there to steal. He had locked her in, and she had had to break out of the window to escape.

I sent for Emily at once. Her story filled out the picture. Pang Tze was quite justified in assuming the girl was in there to steal, because he could not tell the good from the bad. Since he could not touch her, he had locked the door and gone immediately for Emily. Emily was detained by an important case in maternity, and it was a few minutes before she could go to the mess hall and look into the matter. By that time the girl had escaped. Emily had promptly rebuked Pang Tze for locking the door but she, as well as I, approved of his not having laid hands on her. I told Emily to go back to Pang Tze and rebuke him twice as hard from me for what he had done. And the little Hkamti girl was quite satisfied and happy again. What followed, in the events of the morrow and the following days, was no fault of hers although, in theory, she was the cause of the whole mess. She wasn't. Neither was Pang Tze. If neither of them had done anything, these trouble-makers would have found some other happening to exploit.

The next evening I accidentally learned that three-quarters of the nurses were apparently on a hunger strike. Then the two matrons came to me to report the matter and asked me to see the ringleaders, whom they named. When we called them in, one by one, I had the entire staff with me. You can talk to people as individuals in Burma and explain things to their satisfaction, but you cannot do this to a gang. The Number One trouble-maker admitted her fault readily enough but, by the time her interview was finished, Number Two had heard about it and had called a riot squad of nurses (some of whom were just little girls in pre-nurse training) to attack my house.

Number One then joined Number Two, and the entire staff listened to her in awe—as I did myself. Number One had been specializing in the organization of strikes for two years before coming here for training. She had led a strike in Lashio just for the sake of leading a strike. She and Number Two were the most expert rabble-rousers I have ever heard in action—and I do not except even U Saw, who assassinated General Aung San.

The matron called in girls as individuals or in small groups, and we gave them a chance to air their grievances. Each girl or group went away completely mollified. This angered Number Two and Number Three so much that they tried to rush in and break down the door of the conference room, but eventually the four ringleaders gave it up and went home to bed. The quality of our girls was shown by the fact that, aside from the petulant ringleaders, not one nurse failed to be on duty caring for patients when she was supposed to be on duty. They enjoyed the thrill of striking only when off duty.

Two days after the strike, Sao Nyunt Yee, a Buddhist Shan princess, one of the finest girls we had, came with Sarah, a Christian Karen, to tell me that they thought the girls would feel much better if I would fire Pang Tze, since he had long been in the habit of shouting accusations at perfectly innocent girls. I immediately agreed to do so, saying I would have done so at any moment if girls had come to me with concrete proposals in the courteous, respectful way that Sao Nyunt Yee and Sarah always used. You cannot submit to a mob.

What we were trying to do with our Training School from 1946 to 1950 was foredoomed to failure. It simply could not have been done, whether before Independence or after Independence, for now the control of the school was divided. The Government had the final word. In one case they forced me to keep a girl for a year and a half after she should have been expelled. I was long-suffering because the Frontier States were in terrible condition medically. Moreover, prewar experience had shown that if we went about it in the right way we could in many cases make a superb nurse out of originally poor material. The Government had spent a lot of money on the training of these girls, and I did not want that money wasted if I could possibly avoid it. A surgeon who amputates admits he wasn't able to cure the original disease, and I hate to amputate. I hate to be a failure. But my patience cost me dear. With less of it, I might not have gone to jail.

After our strike we should have thrown out all four trouble-makers whether their sponsoring minor politicians liked it or not. There should have been a real showdown. Number One continued to make trouble in spite of her promises to behave, so I gave her transportation back to her family in Lashio. Number Two asked for her annual vacation and disappeared completely. Numbers Three and Four quieted down somewhat on the surface but continued to cause trouble behind the scenes. Eventually they succeeded in having me arrested as a traitor and then lied about me so patently that even the trial court threw out their testimony. If I had expelled them in 1948 events might have been very different, but the nursing school in 1948–1949 was not a completely private institution. It was three-quarters Government. I conceived it my duty to the Government to be patient and to keep on trying to change people's natures.

This also has a distinct bearing: The nurses' training school was 85% Government-financed; the hospital was 85% private. Yet the two institutions were interdependent. If the nurses' training school had received not more than 40% of the budget from Government sources, our effort might have succeeded and I might have kept out of jail. If I could then have had Dr. Ai Lun, the surgeon we had trained to be my assistant, as superintendent of both those institutions, he could have spent a great deal of time chumming around with Government officials and politicians and could have kept informed at first hand and authoritatively as to what was happening. An American could not do this, not without exposing himself to the charge of interference in Burman politics.

10

Burman Politics

THROUGHOUT all of these postwar years the political pot in Burma had been simmering, and in 1946, before the events described in the preceding chapter, it had begun to come to a boil. During the first three months of that year everything began to happen. The British began to act as though they might actually give Burma her independence. It was reported that they were sympathetic to the idea of giving Burma Proper to the Burmese but were resolved on the retention of the Burma Frontier Areas as a British mandate until the Burmese should prove that they could rule in such a way as to persuade these Frontier peoples to join them. So they set up a Frontier Areas Administration to take over as soon as the civil government replaced the British military administration.

The British had always administered these Frontier Areas on a different basis from Burma Proper. The Shan State and the Karenni State, with the sawbwas of the individual states, some forty in number, had been made into a federation. When Burma was separated from India, the Burmese were given their own British-dominated legislative assembly in Rangoon. But this assembly did not control the Federated Shan States and Karenni, which were governed by the Defence Department in Rangoon.

Using only Karens, Karennis, Kachins and Chins in their army, perhaps because they did not want the Burmese and Shans to know too much of modern warfare, the British regarded these races as their special wards and gave them preferential treatment. This had enhanced the centuries-old race prejudices. Perhaps because of their sense of responsibility for the welfare of these special wards of theirs; perhaps because they hoped retention of the Frontier Areas would have a steadying influence on the politicians of a new, independent Burma Proper; perhaps because they were foresighted enough to see that the presence of Great Britain in these Frontier Areas would preclude the threats to Burma by Chinese Communists and Chinese Nationalists which have since developed; perhaps because they wanted complete control of the silver mines at Namtu and the wolfram mines at Mawchi as well as the teak of the Frontier Areas—whatever the motives, Great Britain was proposing a partition of Burma, similar to the partition of India and Pakistan which they later carried out. But unless Britain had retained Moulmein at the mouth of the Salween, these Frontier Areas would have had no outlet except through Independent Burma. For only in its lower reaches is the Salween navigable.

The great Burmese national hero of the postwar days was General Aung San. He was the only leader around whom all of the Burmese had been ready to rally. On his return from Japan, where he had gone with about thirty others to study military matters, he had organized what at the time was called the Burma Independence Army and had led the Burmese resistance movement. This army, which his detractors called his private army, later became the People's

Volunteer Organization. For purposes of government he had organized the Anti-Fascist People's Freedom League. (The term "anti-fascist," which was popular at the time, meant anti-dictator. But at the beginning this was a coalition which included Communists, who certainly believed in dictatorships.) With this organization he had pressed for the independence of all of British Burma.

A great conference took place at Panglong in February, 1947. It made Panglong, in the Shan State, the birthplace of the Union of Burma. General Aung San was present, and it was at this conference that the Chins, Kachins, and Shans had resolved to join him in his plan for a united Burma, completely free from British domination.

Personally, I was by no means downhearted or full of despair at this decision. I was not British. To me union is a gift of God and partition a gift of the devil.

Then came tragedy. In the following July Aung San and half his cabinet were assassinated by fire from machine-guns which had been smuggled into Parliament. He was at the height of his popularity, the only man at that time around whom the Burmese would rally. The assassins also killed my very good friend Mong Pawn, the most advanced thinker and most constructive man in the Shan State. That was an evil day in Burma.

This assassination was the result of the machinations of prewar Prime Minister U Saw, who paid for his evil deeds with his life. The mantle of Aung San then fell upon his friend Thakin Nu, who is now known as U Nu.

During this stormy period I had twice been to the United States on lecture tours, each of which had lasted for six months. But the echoes had reached me. My sister's letters to me in America about the new nurses that were turning up without warning in January and February, 1947, had worried me greatly. Again, on my second lecture tour, Grace's letters made me feel that everything back in Burma was getting still more tense.

One disturbing element in the situation was the Communist and dacoit business. Burma had had no real peace since the war. At first there had been the deserters from the Chinese Nationalist army, who formed gangs and attacked villages up and down the Ledo road and along the Chinese border until the Government let the Kachins loose; the Kachins had either liquidated the Chinese or had driven them back into China where they belonged. Then there were the Burmese bands of dacoits or bandits, banditry being a national habit among ne'er-do-well Burmese who want adventure. At first these operated simply as dacoits and mostly along the Irrawaddi River south of Bhamo and north of Mandalay, where they machine-gunned river boats. They didn't enjoy getting too close to Kachins. Then they spread along the Shan State-Burma Proper border, where the people are hybrids and restless.

Later they began to adopt the name Communist, which had become very stylish, though they knew nothing about Communism and cared less. All they wanted was loot. Later the real Communist leaders of Burma spent a great deal of time indoctrinating them—later I would hear them indoctrinating each other all the time I was in jail. The Commies tried to gather them into as large bands as the Burmese can form and remain loyal to one another when they do not have the leadership of their own great men. When the Communist name began to lose standing a couple of years later, the Commies reversed their tactics. After a raid by Communists, the Communists would excuse themselves to the people by saying the bands were dacoits, not Communists.

Burma was most certainly not a stable country when independence came in January, 1948.

On Independence Day, January 4, 1948, my old friend Sao Shwe Thaike became President of Burma. His status was like that of a president of France. The active leader of the Government was Prime Minister U Nu (Thakin Nu), now one of the most influential figures in the New Asia.

This was an interim government, not based on a ballot. The first general elections in Burma were to be held six months later in July, 1948.

Burma had won her freedom. But with Independence came disunity, disorder, and armed revolt from various rebel forces. Most important among these, at first, were the two separate factions of Communists—the so-called White Flag Communists and the Red Flag Communists—who competed with each other as well as with the socialists, who were trying to be democratic. Both the Reds and the Whites showed signs of attempting to outdo U Saw and obtain power by judicious or injudicious assassination. Luckily for Burma they did not succeed. But instead, they went underground and started the first two insurrections against the Government of Burma. In one way or another these Communists have been fighting the Government ever since. Along with the Communist rebels, the Burmese Army had to fight the remnants of the Chinese Nationalist army, mentioned before, and the motley gangs of dacoits. Finally —and this came later—they had to fight the rebels of the Karen National Defense Organization, the most powerful and persistent of the insurrectionists, whose aim was an autonomous Karen state. So in these years the young republic, eager to achieve unity and move forward economically and politically, led a precarious existence, harassed by civil war.

Into the turmoil that followed Independence I arrived back in Rangoon from my second stay in the States, in April of 1948. This time Mrs. Seagrave, with the two younger boys, followed by freighter, although the political situation threatened to make life at Namkham very different from what it had been in prewar years. How different, we were to learn as time went on and the unrest and tension grew. It was eventually decided that the boys and their mother should return to the United States, where the boys could continue their schooling under more normal conditions.

As soon as I got back, I started off on another surgical tour, and from then on peculiar things happened everywhere. The first was at Loikaw:

Before I left Namkham my mechanic had filled the master cylinder of my brake hydraulic system but apparently had been careless in closing the cap. Suddenly my brakes ceased to exist just as I crossed the bridge between the Shan and Karenni States at dusk and then turned a bend in the road and saw a brand-new gate where a month before there had been none. I was traveling slowly and had no difficulty stopping the car at the exact ten yards from the gate demanded at every other spot in Burma. But it seems there was an invisible new sign on some tree somewhere, requiring cars to stop *twenty* yards away. By the time I had stopped, soldiers had rifles, carbines, and a Sten gun trained on me and their officer, apparently a newly created second lieutenant, was screaming at me. I put my head out of the car and called out:

"What have I done wrong?"

That tore it. The officer, who from his accent was not Burmese, came to my window and began to revile me in the most efficient putrid Burmese I have ever heard. He must have had a quart of 98-proof alcohol in his system, judging by the fumes which overpowered me. When I told him who I was and what I was doing there and offered him my passport, it merely incensed him the more. I was wondering what treatment we could use for apoplexy when he stomped off into the trees. The guns were still at aim—not just at the ready. So all nine of us tried to relax while we waited for another half hour. Then a truck came out of the woods and turned on the road beyond the gate. In it was mounted a Bren gun, with several soldiers and their rifles for support.

The lieutenant then came back, dressed in parade uniform. After devoting ten minutes more to a dissertation on my crimes, he ordered me to follow him to Loikaw at a distance of exactly fifty yards. If at any time I increased or decreased that distance, he said, the Bren gunner, had orders to open fire. Now, with my brakes, this was somewhat of an order. I could not have carried it out had I not known practically every inch of that road. The order was exceedingly difficult to obey, because the lieutenant's driver was drunk, too, and he kept stopping and starting for no good reason at all. I hand it to those eight Shan, Kachin, and Karen girls. Not one of them turned a hair.

At Loikaw the truck turned into the Union Military Police lines and stopped. So did I—at fifty yards. The lieutenant disappeared in the direction of town and there was another forty minutes' wait. Then:

"Sorry this had to happen, Doctor," said a courteous voice beside me, and I turned to see two Burmese officers, who had walked up from behind. "There are new rules and everyone is afraid. Absolute obedience is necessary."

"I'm sorry I broke your rules," I said. "There was no gate a month ago."

"That's all right. Hope you're not angry. The lieutenant was drunk."

"I'm not angry. Is it all right to go on with my trip and hospital work?"

"Yes, indeed."

The officers saluted and we backed out. The second lieutenant never reappeared. The incident ended smoothly, but it left an uneasy feeling with us all.

Dr. Phyllis Krasu was still in the Loikaw Hospital—a fine person whom I had known well for many years. There was not much surgery, but she told us a bit of what had been happening. The old sawbwa of Bawlake had gone insane, and his young son had not yet been enthroned. In the interim, Bawlake's "strong man" was a man named U Bee, a "short-necked" Padaung Baptist. (It is the non-Christian Padaungs who stretch the necks of their women and tour with Ringling Brothers and Barnum & Bailey.) Most of the Padaungs on the fringe of Loikaw are Baptists; those who live farther northwest are Roman Catholic.

Dr. Phyllis told us that trouble was brewing between the Baptist and the Catholic Padaungs. U Bee was a dictatorial scoundrel and very overbearing in his dealings with the Catholics. According to rumor, the Catholics also had a strong man, a priest, but whether this was true or not, it is true that the Catholics were fed up with U Bee, and shortly before our arrival they had come down and shot up and burned his village. Many innocents were killed, but not U Bee. He had come to Loikaw, and when we arrived there he was in protective custody of the Burma Government.

There was a sequel to this incident. At first it came to us as rumor; later the events were confirmed. It was said that U Bee had been abducted from his protective custody, had had certain portions of his anatomy amputated, had been then sewn up in a sack with a large rock and dropped into the Bilu River. When this news came to the ears of a certain Karen Baptist battalion serving on the border of Kengtung State, they were not pleased. They decided to take vengeance on the Catholic Padaungs on whom they blamed the deed. When their officers objected, they shot two of them; then, threatening to blow up the Sawbwa with hand grenades, they took trucks, enjoined radio silence, got to Loilem and surrounded the treasury and Government offices. Fortified with the treasury money, they went on down to Karenni and beat up the Padaungs. (It is said that they repaid the money they took from the Loilem treasury after their punitive foray.)

The Baptist-Catholic troubles caused me to postpone my next surgical tour to Loikaw. I did finally go, having been told I could if I reported to the colonel in command there, but found the place half deserted. Things were tense. There was a feeling of war in the air. Yet it was impossible to foresee that the recent troubles would turn into open rebellion against the Government, as happened only two days after I left.

The Karen Rebellion

THE TIME of my troubles—troubles intimately related to the uprising of the Karens—was now fast approaching.

The Karen-Burmese conflicts are age-old. In some ways they are similar in origin to those of the racial issue in the United States. The Burmese vastly outnumber the Karens of Burma Proper. Burmese had conquered Karens repeatedly, centuries ago, and the Karens had been in more or less of a state of servitude to the Burmese until the British had forcibly freed them in the First and Second Burmese Wars. The Burmese had resented this forcible improvement in the status of the Karens, much as Americans in the South resented the emancipation of the Negroes. A further improvement in the status of Karens was the result of their acceptance of Christianity at the hands of American Baptist missionaries; this, too, did nothing to improve Karen-Burmese relations. But worst of all was the fact that the British used the Karens to police the country. That the British also used Indian, Punjabi, Gurkha, Kachin, and Chin troops did not alter this resentment. Nor did the fact that Karens never reached the highest level in government, though their capabilities fully warranted the top level.

The Japanese occupation did not help matters. During the occupation, restraints were removed and several massacres of Karens by Burmese in the Irrawaddi delta were reported. Like American lynchings, these reports were far more sensational than were any reports of *good* Karen-Burmese relations. On one Karen New Year's Day Prime Minister U Nu, in a speech to Karens, acknowledged in public that this action of "bad Burmese" had a causative relationship to the present trouble with "bad Karens." U Nu's speech showed him to be a statesman of the first rank.

Like all the other racial groups in Burma, the Karens had been stirred by the waves of nationalism which had been sweeping through the East since V-J Day. They were now determined to have their own autonomous state. This had led to the formation of the Karen National Defense Organization.

Under General Aung San during the year 1946 the Burmese had handled the Shan, Kachin, and Chin nationalists with a great deal of statesmanship—more statesmanship than the colonial British showed. General Aung San realized that Burma would hardly be Burma, and would certainly not be a safe Burma, without the Frontier States.

Ultimately all this politicking took care of the proposed British Frontier Areas except for the Salween District. The Salween District is one of the poor areas of Burma. It will need a lot of enlightened scientific development before it becomes self-supporting. It is the only area in Burma where the Karens are in a majority, but it contains the poorest and most backward Karens of all. It could not exist alone as an autonomous or as a British-dominated state, and therefore, when the British pulled out of Burma, it remained a district in Burma.

A great deal of trouble would have been spared Burma, and the Communist rebellions would have been wiped out, with the help of the Karens, long before they were, if the British had joined at a round table with General Aung San and his party and with the great Karen leaders—for there are not a few great Karens—and had sat there until a state had been outlined geographically which would have satisfied the Karens' nationalist aspirations and still have been acceptable to the Burmese. A team of Karens is said to have gone to London to argue with Attlee's government. They could more profitably have talked directly to Aung San and have made some concessions. Aung San would undoubtedly have made some concessions too, as he had to the Kachins and the Shans.

The trouble was that the Karens demanded just too much. They were seeking Tenasserim's tin and rubber, Moulmein's port, Toungoo's access to wolfram, and Irrawaddi's rice. And they were demanding too much from a race which had dominated them from time immemorial until the British had taken up the cudgels in their behalf and then left them out on a limb.

Terror may have had something to do with Burmese refusal to make a decent but firm offer to the Karens while the offering was good. It should be remembered that in 1945–1948 the Karens had the greatest number of British-trained, battle-tested troops in Burma as well as a great reserve of retired men and officers, and that the Commander-in-Chief of Burma during the entire first year of Independence was a Karen—Major-General Smith Dun. The Burmese may have feared retaliation of a forcible sort. Heaven only knows what went on behind the scenes.

But the fact remains that the British pulled out of Burma without having in any way settled the most important problem of all—how the Karens and the Burmese were to get along together, a million and a half Karens versus at least twelve million Burmese.

Then the Communist insurrection started, and the troops which fought the Communists most fiercely and successfully were Karen troops. For when Karens shot and killed Burma's Communists they were not shooting and killing other Karens or Kachins or Chans or Chins or Nagas or Lahus or Was. They were shooting and killing Burmese—who happened to be Communists. Racial antagonism was then stronger than politics.

The next thing that happened was the massacre of Karens at Mergui, apparently on Christmas Day, 1948. For some reason, despite the fact that Karen troops were successfully engaged in putting down the Communists, the Government had decided to disarm all Karens. The story runs that a Burmese officer was sent to Mergui at the southern end of the Tenasserim Peninsula, with orders to disarm all Karens in the district. The officer may have been afraid of the Karens; he may have thought his action would gain him a decoration. At any rate, it is said that he waited until all Karens were at Christmas services; then his men set up Bren guns near several churches and mowed down men, women, and children as they came out.

This terrifying episode inevitably led to reprisals, the first at Ahlone (where my childhood was spent), the second at Insein. Briefly, as related to me by Burmese, these are the alleged facts:

It was after the Mergui massacre that the Lower Burma Karens changed the name of their nationalist organization from the Karen National Union to the Karen National Defense Organization, the word "defense" implying a threat that they would no longer merely "take it to the Lord in prayer." Probably this was a mistake, and it may indicate why the Karen Quarter at Ahlone began to notice increased hostility on the part of the Burmese all around them. The Karen leader at Ahlone therefore went to the Karen Commander-in-Chief, General Smith Dun, and obtained a company or two of Karen troops to patrol Ahlone. Then came the night when it was discovered that the patrolling was being done by Burmese troops and not by Karens. Since World War II, Negro Americans have fought in the line with white Americans in the same regiments and companies. If the Burma Army from British times had been organized in this way instead of in separate battalions for each race, there might have been no insurrections in Burma at all in this past decade. At any rate, that night shooting broke out, and by morning the place was a shambles.

This led to the incident at Insein. Here a battalion of Karen troops had just returned to garrison duty after successful operations against the Communist rebels forty miles north of Rangoon. Expecting to receive the thanks of a grateful Government, they were offended at being ordered to lay down their arms. Then the shooting at Ahlone occurred. The garrison at Insein rebelled.

In spite of being shelled from cannon placed near the University of Rangoon and from gunboats on the Rangoon River, Insein held out for several weeks. Karen troops from all over the delta slipped into Insein in spite of the efforts of their senior officers who were faithful to their oath to defend the Government of Burma. One of these senior officers was the husband of our Dr. Ba Saw's sister, Dr. Helen Dwe. The hotheads in this officer's command decided to proceed to Insein. On being ordered to obey their oath to the Government, they shot their officer and went to Insein anyway.

I am told that after the Insein tragedy had continued some time, a truce was arranged between the wiser Karen leaders and the Government which was satisfactory to both sides. But the hotheads would not tolerate any truce and kept on fighting the Government.

The Karen National Defense Organization was convinced that they could conquer Burma. They could not seem to realize that their troops would have access only to captured or smuggled arms and ammunition while the Government, as the legitimate government of the country, would have access to world markets. They must have counted on being joined in their revolt by all the well-disciplined, battle-tested Kachin and Chin and even Gurkha troops—a futile hope, for if senior Karen officers had refused to break their oath of allegiance, certainly few Kachin and Chin officers would consent to break theirs.

To me only one explanation of the Karen persistence makes sense: The Karens badly underestimated the Burmese. In and out of jail I have heard the Karen statement that the Burmese are incapable of loyalty to their leaders. That statement has been disproved again and again during these difficult times. But at the beginning of the rebellion, and even before that, there had been evidences of real disloyalty among the Burmese troops. To begin the troubles, the leaders of the Red Flag and White Flag Communists, formerly closely associated with General Aung San, had broken faith and started their Communist rebellions against the Government. Then, during the fighting at Insein, unit after unit of Burmese troops, when ordered to attack Insein, slipped away into the jungle. Their disloyalty and that of others undoubtedly gave great encouragement to the Karen insurgents, who continued fighting even though it led to intense misery for the hundreds of thousands of loyal Karens.

At this time I knew very little about all that was going on in Burma. Even now it is impossible to realize how little I knew. I have several excuses to offer.

In the first place I was intensely busy. Our hospital was jammed with serious cases. Then, there was great irregularity in the mail services, as a result of all these insurrections. It did not pay to try to get newspapers from Rangoon, because they came either irregularly or not at all. Even my subscriptions to American periodicals failed to show up. Of eight subscriptions I had placed for the *Reader's Digest* for myself and my friends, only four copies showed up during that whole year of 1949. The Burma Broadcasting Service was Government-controlled, and one cannot expect a Government radio to tell you *all* the bad news. Besides, my radio was out of whack, and my sister's only worked sporadically. Of rumors there were no end, but these I refused to believe unless they were confirmed by several independent sources.

From the days of the Communist rebellion, transportation from Rangoon to Namkham had become more and more difficult and more and more costly. At first, rail transportation was cut only occasionally: We had periods of considerable delay, but eventually supplies arrived. But by the time of the Karen uprising there was no transportation at all except by air from Rangoon to Bhamo or Lashio, with trucks from those points on. On one occasion we had to spend twenty dollars for one gallon of gasoline. (The regular price in Namkham is one dollar a gallon.) We had to give up electricity, and then we had to give up all motor travel except to save life. Later, river traffic to Bhamo was resumed and the price of gas came down, but all these hazards and difficulties had the effect of isolating us from the outside world.

Much of the information I now have about these events I picked up in jail while awaiting my trial. There was nothing to do but listen to people talk, and the Karen rebellion and Communist insurrections were the prime topic of all the conversations which I overheard.

A good example of how, in those days, I learned what was happening was my experience when I first heard about the massacre of the Karens at Mergui.

That day I had been driving an American ambulance with a weapons-carrier chassis for three hundred miles over bad roads, and the eight nurses on board were clamoring for a halt so eagerly that I drove into the pastor's compound in Lashio. His house was brilliantly lit and crowded with people. Some kind of service seemed to be going on, but a man came downstairs at the sound of the ambulance.

"What's going on?" I asked wearily.

"A lot of Karens were massacred at Mergui," he replied, "and we have been taking it to the Lord in prayer."

"Taking it to the Lord in prayer" had always been a Karen habit since first they accepted Christianity in the time of my great-grandparents. It never occurred to me then that they would take any other action with regard to their hereditary troubles with the Burmese.

What now follows is a rough picture painted by a dozen brushes. One of the brushes, however, was wielded by no less a man than the rebel leader Naw Seng. This was the gentleman who was later to cause all my troubles. Some of the steps in his rise came about as follows:

North of Toungoo, the Burmese Army was successfully fighting the Communists when an uprising occurred at Toungoo. The Karen insurgents took over the city. The Army colonel up north was ordered to break contact with the Communists and drive south to contain the Karens at Toungoo. He sent Captain Naw Seng ahead with his first troops. The next thing the colonel knew, Naw Seng had reappeared with his own and a lot of Karen troops, held up his own colonel and demanded that he join the Karen rebels. This the colonel refused to do and was taken captive.

Naw Seng was next heard of at Meiktila airstrip, where he and his men nonchalantly welcomed two C-47 transport planes that innocently landed there. When the pilots, who were said to have been British, stepped out of their planes they were surrounded by Naw Seng's men holding Sten guns, and ordered to fly two platoons of rebels to Maymyo airport. At the airport no one was suspicious, and Naw Seng soon had control of the field. His men were dispersed in a manner which must have appeared perfectly normal from the air, because a Burma Air Force bomber, followed soon by a fighter, did not hesitate to land. Both planes were taken over by Naw Seng.

He and his men then proceeded in an innocent-seeming manner to Maymyo, where they persuaded a fairly large number of troops to join the rebellion and demanded the surrender of the Burmese and Gurkha garrisons. Whatever the reason, all this went like clockwork, and the Kachins and Karens took over the city, the old summer capital of Burma.

Naw Seng later said he had captured a secret document

which he claimed was called "Operation Aung San." This operation purported to direct that first the Karens, then the Kachins, then the Chins, and then the Shans, etc., were to be eliminated. For his own purposes Naw Seng chose to believe that this meant that these races were to be "liquidated" in the Russian sense. A Maymyo officer whom I met later denied that this could have been the meaning. If, in fact, any such document ever really existed, he said, it probably meant that the Government desired to train sufficient Burmese troops to defend the country, and only then to eliminate Karen, Kachin, and Chin battalions *as such* from the Army, as the United States has now eliminated all-Negro units. This latter explanation must have been the correct one, because it is now being implemented.

At any rate, Naw Seng seized upon his own interpretation and soon organized what he termed the Karen-Kachin National Defense Organization rebellion. Then he turned his attention to Mandalay. Leaving a Karen-Kachin garrison at Maymyo, he marched down on totally unprepared Mandalay and captured the town.

Here he left a company or so of his Karen troops in the Fort, told the authorities to continue to administer the town, and started south to rejoin the Karens at Toungoo, who were said to be waiting only for his arrival before they began their drive down on Insein and Rangoon. What the Karens at Toungoo did not realize was that success had gone to Naw Seng's head and that he was now full of ideas of grandeur, the beginning of the symptoms of insanity which I saw in him later. Up to this point the Karens had had complete control of the element of surprise. Thanks to Naw Seng they now lost it, for when he reached Meiktila and Thazi he found a small force of loyal Government troops in the neighborhood. Instead of by-passing them he had to stop to show off, and fought uselessly for several days. The delay dispersed some of his troops and gave the Army time to get a battalion over from Moulmein, and the Karens gave up.

This was the end of the Mandalay and Maymyo occupation, and the Government of Burma again started ordering all things properly for Burma.

Things then seemed quiet for months, and I went placidly about my medical duties, little realizing that I myself was about to be drawn into the chaos which was then Burma.

12

Naw Seng at Namkham

MY TROUBLES really began in June and July of 1949. We still had a branch dispensary at Muse, eighteen miles away. In this dispensary there were a senior and a junior nurse who were under the administration of a municipal committee in each town. Grace assigned the nurses and we were responsible for their professional work. In June Grace assigned as senior nurse at Muse a Karen girl who became fascinated by some young Burmese gentlemen stationed in the town and flirted with them outrageously, entertaining them in her quarters. The town and the committee were scandalized and demanded that we recall her at once. This we did, replacing her with another Karen girl who had never caused us a bit of trouble. But no sooner had this second girl reached Muse than she surpassed the first one in all respects, and the committee came to me again, gnashing their teeth and tearing their hair. So she was recalled, and then, in desperation, our matron sent her own sister, a Chan girl, as first nurse. The committee was immediately pacified.

But the young Burmese gentlemen were very displeased and wrote a seventeen-page letter to the matron in which they accused her of lack of patriotism and of disloyalty to Burma because of the fact that her sister's charms were not placed at their disposal. They did not attack me directly to my face, but I was told a long while after that they had written savage reports about me to Rangoon.

By this time my old associate in the hospital, Dr. Ba Saw, had come back from America. I notified the Shan Government authorities in Rangoon of his arrival and they showed him every courtesy, making it possible for him to bring his sister, Dr. Helen Dwe, up to Namkham. At Namkham, Ba Saw assumed his full duties, teaching the younger doctors the new procedures he had learned in America. He was upset about the rebellion in the Karenni State and proposed that he send his sister Dr. Helen to Taunggyi to buy a plot of ground there and build a house. He and his family could live there while he conducted private practice in Taunggyi until such time as Government troops should recapture the Karenni State and make it possible for him to work for his beloved Karens. Since this involved no disloyalty to the Government which had been so courteous to him, I gave my approval, and Dr. Helen left immediately for Taunggyi in July. We all expected Karenni to be retaken in a matter of weeks.

It must have been about the middle of August, 1949, that we heard the Karens had captured Taunggyi, the capital of the Shan State. Then quiet returned again. But not for long.

Late one night, Dr. Ba Saw came to my house, bringing with him every Karen male of the neighborhood. Never have I seen people so jittery. They had heard a rumor that all the Karens were being rounded up and taken to jail. They were quite willing to be arrested, they said, if the arrests were made by the proper Union Government or Shan State Government officials. However, the report was that the Burmese were having a free-for-all and that unauthorized Burmese were venting their spite on the Karens. This they would not tolerate. Unless I guaranteed that they would be arrested only by the proper authorities they were going to take to the woods.

"How much do you expect one lone American to do?" I asked. "I have no authority except what prestige I may have as a doctor who has served this country for a long time. My prestige didn't help a bit in that trouble in the Muse dispensary. I can't guarantee a thing. But you had better think very carefully before you do anything as serious as taking to the woods."

The Karens promised to do nothing hasty, but by the next morning every single one of them had disappeared. That really put me on the spot. I stopped everything and made out a written report. Then I took it personally to the office of the Shweli Amat, the administrator of this part of the State. The Amat was not in, so I gave the report to his Burmese clerk and came home.

Several hours later I was visited by the Amat and by the chief police officer of the valley. Both of them were greatly disturbed. They had received orders from Lashio to arrest all Karen males and take them in for screening. It was their opinion that the Karens connected with me were so well known that if I, together with some local official, were to write out guarantees for their conduct and loyalty, the authorities would release them at once. But if the Karens did not yield by six in the morning, they said, the fat would be in the fire. For their part they would guarantee to arrest the Karens and transport them to Hsenwi themselves. Did I know where the Karens were?

"No," I said, "I don't know where they are, and their

wives claim they don't know where they intended to go. But in 1942, when the Japanese took over the country, these same Karens took shelter in various Kachin villages in the jungle. They have probably done that again. I can find out the names of those Kachin villages and send schoolboys out at once on the chance of finding them."

The two officials agreed unhappily that that was the best that could be done. Then they left. They had barely disappeared when a viciously angry Kachin *duwa* (chief) burst into my house.

"What's this I hear about the Government arresting faithful Karens who have given their lives in service to our people?" he demanded.

"Hold everything!" I said. "I'll bet it's your village where they are hiding. Isn't it?"

"Yes," he said, truculently.

"O.K. You take a letter back to Ba Saw for me. If they behave themselves and come back here before morning the Shweli Amat and the chief police officer will escort them personally to Hsenwi for screening. If they don't come back, it will be just too bad for us all."

The duwa calmed down a bit. I wrote the letter and sent him halfway to his village in a jeep, with instructions to the driver to wait at the end of the jeep trail until Ba Saw and company returned.

It was two in the morning before the runaways showed up, but they obeyed orders and were on hand at six o'clock with conduct guarantees from myself and a town official. They were taken into custody and started off for Hsenwi while their wives and families took refuge in the lower story of the nurses' home. At Hsenwi the men were screened and released on the strength of my guarantees.

My neck was protruding farther and farther, but I thought I was helping the country! These men had served their country selflessly, not only in British times but since Independence, and not one of them had ever demanded the salary he was worth.

Then on the morning of September third our peace and quiet were shattered by another rumor. This one said that the insurgents were in Lashio and that they might come north to Namkham. Again I discounted the rumor.

However, I was worried. Some very strange things had been happening in Burma, and this rumor might prove to be true. If so, I conceived that the greatest danger to us would be that the Karens might commandeer our trucks, weapons-carriers, and jeeps, and the large store of gasoline which I had had flown up from Rangoon. I called my mechanics and ordered them to bury all our gasoline drums in our woods and to pull off and bury the wheels of all our vehicles except the De Soto and one jeep. The jeep was to have four gallons of gas in the tank to handle our usual emergency calls. These orders were carried out so literally that when, on hearing that the townspeople were taking off for the tall timber, I drove down to Namkham to rescue our nurses there, I did not have enough gas to drive the De Soto up the hill. My mechanic had to bring the jeep down and siphon a gallon of his gas into my tank before I could make it.

That evening a lot of jeeps and trucks drove past the hospital, heading for Bhamo. Rumor said that all the Burmese officials from Hsenwi North were fleeing to Bhamo because the Karens were reported to be killing Burmese officials on sight, whereas other people were being left strictly alone. I wouldn't know. The fact remains that hardly a single Burmese was to be seen for some time thereafter. But the Burmese women and children, whom the men had left behind for lack of transport, and a lot of Indians and Indo-Burmans as well as a few Chans came up to me and asked to take refuge under my wing. How much influence I might have with the insurgents I did not know. But it seemed difficult to believe that Karens would shoot out of hand the great-grandson of the man who had brought them their Christianity. All I could promise the refugees was that they would be hurt over my dead body. That seemed to satisfy them and they camped out on the floors in the medical and maternity buildings and in the nurses' home.

About two o'clock in the morning I was awakened by the sound of a jeep which could not be persuaded to climb the steep road up to the hospital. After twenty minutes of futile effort it gave up the battle and I dropped off to sleep, only to be wakened by Dr. Ba Saw shaking my shoulder. I used to sleep behind unlocked doors in those days. I have not done so since the insurgents came to town.

"That Burmese official in the medical ward who has been recovering from typhoid fever is jittery," he said. "A jeep came to take him to Bhamo but it broke down and, in any case, he doesn't think he has the strength to undertake the journey. He asked me to intercede with you. He wants you to guarantee his safety if the insurgents should really come to town."

"Listen," I said. "That fellow has been causing all kinds of trouble, both with other patients and with the nurses on duty. That doesn't matter. But he sports an automatic. Sunday morning he went to church sporting that automatic. If the Karens should come and find him with that automatic I wouldn't be able to do anything for him. If he gives me the gun I will give him a receipt for it, lock it up in the bottom of our hospital files, and give him the same guarantee I gave the others, that the insurgents will hurt him only over my dead body. If he doesn't promise to behave, I can't help him."

At six Ba Saw woke me up again and gave me the automatic. The official was given a receipt, and as soon as the insurgents were driven out by the Army, he got his gun back again. He remained in the neighborhood for months, showing his gratitude by making an unmitigated nuisance of himself.

Later that morning of the fourth, the Lashio garrison passed through town on their way to Bhamo. The soldiers were not fighting a rearguard action. They were not even in a hurry. They stopped their vehicles at the foot of the hospital hill, where there are a number of tea shops and restaurants, and had refreshments. They had their families with them. The Colonel's wife had been a patient of ours. I saw her come up our hill to say goodbye to her nurse friends. She reported that they were being transferred to Myitkyina. Actually they did not go farther than the other side of the American-built Bailey suspension bridge over the Shweli River. There they dug in, as we found out the next day.

That afternoon two Americans, Mr. and Mrs. Dashiell, suddenly appeared. They were Fulbright exchange scholars who had been working in Taunggyi. Now at last we were given some real information and not rumors. The embassy had heard of the capture of Taunggyi by the insurgents and had sent officials to evacuate the Americans. No Americans serving on United States money were to be allowed in any area dominated by insurgents. All had driven north to Lashio, whence some of the Americans had gone on to Rangoon. Mr. and Mrs. Dashiell had come on to Namkham with the idea of continuing on to Bhamo or Myitkyina if the insurgents came to Namkham. On the trip north from Taunggyi the Dashiells had been first in the middle of the Karen column, then in the retreating Army column, and then between the two. Neither side had interfered with their progress. They reached Namkham just behind the Army and just ahead of the rebels.

The Karen rebels must have reached Namkham that same evening, soon after the Dashiells. But they stopped northeast of our hospital, apparently in the area of the Government's reception bungalow for travelers, for I saw nothing of them, though two or three jeeps passed back and forth along the Ledo Road at the foot of our hill. Since the rebels had come to Namkham the Dashiells tried next day to go on to Bhamo but were stopped at the Shweli suspension bridge by the Army's roadblocks.

Two things happened almost simultaneously on the morning of September fifth, while I was lecturing to nurses. As I recall, the first was the arrival of an official Government station-wagon. It passed the door of the White House and stopped under the three banyan trees where everybody parks. From the excited whispers of the Shan girls from Hsenwi State out in front of me and the cries of other Hsenwi nurses outside I guessed that it must be the Commissioner of the Shan State. So I dismissed my class and went out to welcome him.

A wave of relief passed over me, because as far as my work

was concerned he *was* the Government. It was the same feeling that comes over a young surgeon in trouble when an older, more experienced surgeon comes into the operating room and takes over the final responsibility for the life of the patient. I felt now that if I obeyed his orders I would be free from further responsibility. But this was a mistake.

As usual I invited the Commissioner to put up in my house, and he accepted my invitation. According to him there was to be an important conference of the officials of the Frontier States. There were two ends in view: If the Frontier States should agree to unite, they would have a strong position vis-a-vis the Union Government, which would mean that the insurgents would lay down their arms and again become decent citizens. The possible end of this stupid insurrection sounded like something worth working for. But this was internal politics, something for Burmans to handle themselves and something I wanted most definitely to keep out of. Courtesy to the Government representative was my job.

I left the Commissioner chatting with the Dashiells and went over toward the nurses' home to round up the Hsenwi State girls and have them see that their sawbwa was well housed and well fed.

I had no more than reached the banyan trees when a jeep drove up and stopped in front of me. A Kachin Government official whom I had known from his boyhood stepped down and introduced me to two or three Karen insurgent leaders and to a Kachin named Naw Seng. The Karens called this chap Brigadier Naw Seng. I didn't know him from Adam—Naw Seng is the name of about every sixteenth Kachin in the Shan States; it means "number two male jewel." It was months later before I learned that here before me was the Naw Seng who had captured Maymyo and Mandalay. And it was not until I was on trial that I learned that his true rank was that of captain. People called him brigadier, so I automatically called him brigadier, too. Soldiers in all countries are sensitive of their rank, and I didn't want to get into more trouble with the insurgents than I could avoid.

These insurgent leaders repeated the statement made by the Commissioner about the purposes of their meeting at Namkham almost word for word. So I supposed everything was straight and aboveboard. I took the opportunity, however, to state that I had Burmese on the premises who had taken refuge with me and that I expected the rebels to honor my guarantees for their immunity. I had sufficient prestige then, and the rebels agreed not to interfere in any way. They kept their promise—this time.

Naw Seng was clearly in command, the Karens being with him as advisers. As soon as I could I got rid of the gentlemen and went about my professional duties.

On the evening of that day when I first met Naw Seng, Dr. Ba Saw sent word that he was giving a dinner to the Karens and that he wished me to come. Now, I knew Ba Saw's attachment to his own people. When he had first come to me to learn surgery, in 1937, he had told me that when he felt he knew enough surgery he would want to go to a Karen area and serve Karens. His parents had been Karen missionaries to the Chins and he had been born in the Chin Hills. His sister, also a doctor, was working for the Burmese. He himself had worked for Shans and Kachins. He felt, he said, that at least one of the family should work for the Karens and that it would have to be himself. When we evacuated Burma in World War II, he had gone with us to India just in order to be available to help rebuild our shattered work at Namkham after the war. Yet even then he had reminded me that he wanted to be released for Karen work as soon as I could spare him. I could spare him in 1947, but he had done so much for Burma as a whole during the war and for the Shan State both before and after the war that I begged him to take a year of postgraduate work in Louisville General Hospital as a sign of the gratitude I felt for what he had done for Burma and for the unit. Before leaving for America he had indicated to me that he had considered the matter and felt that the Karenni State needed him more than any other Karen area.

These few Karen leaders were the first who had visited Namkham since Ba Saw's return from Louisville, and in view of the apparent legality of their presence in Namkham, it was not surprising to me that he should want to entertain educated men of his own race. I detest going out to dinners here because outside food usually causes either a relapse of my dysentery or a new attack. And I was further unhappy when I received Ba Saw's invitation because I felt that all these marvelous conferences had interfered about enough with our hospital schedule. If the invitation had been from anyone but Ba Saw, for whom I had a very deep respect, or if it had not been Ba Saw's first invitation to me since his return, I would not have gone, but since it was his invitation and since the Commissioner of the Shan State was a guest in my house, I went—and came away as soon as I decently could.

The next morning Ba Saw came to me again. He had heard that there was no further trouble going on in the Shan State and that it was possible for him to carry out his original in-

tention and move to Taunggyi to practice until the Karenni
State mess was cleaned up. I reminded him that I had
guaranteed that he would make no move without Government permission. He would have to see the Commissioner,
and the Commissioner would have to give me a written
release from that obligation before he could do a thing.

The Commissioner knew all about Ba Saw and his plans;
I had told him about them long before the trouble had
broken out in the Karenni State. The Dashiells were present
when I took Ba Saw over to see the Commissioner. It was
later claimed that I had coerced the Commissioner into
releasing me from my guarantee about Ba Saw. This was
really funny. All my guns were locked up in a closet in the
bedroom occupied by the Commissioner, and his bodyguard
was sitting armed just outside the window. Besides, the
Commissioner is no coward. He agreed to let Ba Saw go
and promised to send the signed release later.

Meanwhile, the Dashiells were worried about their
responsibility to the Embassy, since Namkham was full of
the insurgents. With permission from the Commissioner,
they went back on their tracks and out to a lovely valley
called Mong Paw, away from the Burma Road, where they
could continue their studies until the rebels left.

13

Seeds of Disaster

DURING the days that the conference was waiting for the Kachin State delegation to arrive, the great football game took place. It took place, of course, on our football ground. I had just finished my last lecture of the day and was sitting on the back steps of the White House watching the sunset when a boisterous group of young men from the town started down the hill.

"What's been going on?" I asked the nurse, idly.

"They say the townspeople and the insurgents have been having a football match," she replied.

This football game—so unimportant to me at the time —was later made a part of the charges which were made against me under the High Treason Act. It was alleged that by allowing the insurgents to hold a football match on hospital premises I had "aided and comforted Naw Seng and his followers when [I] knew they were committing High Treason." Actually, it had taken place without my knowledge or consent.

During these days when the Commissioner was staying in my home, Naw Seng and the Karen leaders dropped in two or three times to see me in the little stone house where I was staying. What they came about was to argue about nurses. Their idea was that whether this Namkham Conference was a success or not, I should furnish them with nurses to take care of their sick. I just laughed at them. They were going to get no nurses under my jurisdiction.

Once they came in the early morning while I was enjoying my coffee, American style. My sister and the others had finished, but my coffee is a part of my religion; I take more time over my coffee than over my dinner, because it is then that I try to find the answers to all my problems and make a mental program for my day's work. The rebels came in and sat in the only chairs, those around the table. There were coffee cups all around the gentlemen, but they were served no coffee by me—I always drain the pot—and they certainly got no tea, which I detest and almost never have in the house. Nevertheless, this very unsocial gathering was later presented as a report that I had had them there *on invitation* and was giving them a tea-party. This became another of the charges against me for treason.

It must have been three days after the arrival of the rebels before the official delegation from the Kachin State came to the conference. The Chins never did turn up. I knew two of the Kachins well. One was the grandfather of a staff nurse who was here at the time. I went to none of their conferences, and nobody told me a word about what went on. I did not find out for months that the reason for the conference's breaking up was that the Kachins had rightly demanded that Naw Seng and his men all lay down their arms before any further subjects were discussed. I did not even know that the conference *had* broken up until someone came to my door the next morning and said that the Commissioner had gone and had left a paper for me. That paper was the signed release from my guarantees for Ba Saw.

The next thing I knew, everybody, official and otherwise, had left. When I went down into the town to see about the Namkham nurses I saw not a soul—only a couple of Chinese beggars looking hopefully for something to loot. Naw Seng and company had also left. From Ba Saw I heard that Naw Seng had left a platoon of his best soldiers under a major who lived at the Government bungalow at Man Hkam, the village northeast of the hospital.

Their departure coincided with the breaking out of mortar fire from the suspension bridge. That afternoon Emily came running to me saying that a panic had started among the nurses and that they were rolling up their bedding and planning to take to the woods. I asked her to gather them all in the nurses' ballroom and insisted that all the staff nurses be present.

The gist of my speech was this: First, during the occupation by the insurgents there had been no panic and no one had been hurt. Our war experience had proved that it was the people who ran who were hurt. They had not yet run, and they had not yet been hurt; but if they ran now, they would be hurt. Second, we had been behaving during the previous days in accordance with the instructions of the Commissioner. Every Government officer, Union, State, and Local, had left us in the lurch, and there was no way now to contact the Government in Rangoon. All we could do was continue to act as the Commissioner had desired. Third, why were they in a panic now that their Army was returning to retake Namkham, as if they were afraid that their own Army would shoot them up? I said that no matter which Kachin battalion might be approaching, some of the soldiers in that battalion would be their own relatives, and they would certainly not fire on the nurses or allow them to be hurt. Fourth, the Government of Burma was legitimate and would not allow their Army to fire on a hospital. Finally, I said, it had taken about sixteen five-hundred-pound bombs to destroy one wing and the front of the Harper Memorial Surgical building during World War II. Now there were no bombs being dropped; only mortars were being used. If they stayed in the lower story of their nurses' home, away from the windows, I would guarantee no one would be hurt even if the Army made a mistake and did shell us.

Then I went home. In half an hour Emily reported that the nurses were quiet and that the panic was over.

But not for long. The next morning I received a letter from the Commissioner. He said that he had been taken ill on his return to Kutkai and he asked me to send Dr. Ba Saw to prescribe for him, and his sister-in-law, a nurse, to take care of him. A jeep was furnished for transportation. They left immediately.

Ba Saw did not return until about nine that night. He immediately went to Dr. Tu's house to inquire about the welfare of his patients. While he was there he heard Mrs. Tu saying she had a report that the Commissioner had been arrested and jailed by Naw Seng. Realizing what havoc a rumor like this would cause if the Shan nurses heard it, and knowing, as I did, that Mrs. Tu enjoyed nothing better than spreading rumors, Dr. Ba Saw came to me much disturbed. He had just left the Commissioner and the Commissioner had most definitely *not* been arrested. (Much later we learned that he was arrested the day after Mrs. Tu had claimed that his arrest had already taken place.)

I was so fed up with her rumor-mongering proclivities and was so apprehensive of another incipient panic that I wrote her a note warning her not to spread any such rumor. I used English which she could not fail to understand, with the result that the letter did not make pleasant reading in court, where it became the basis of the second charge against me.

Then came the big day when Namkham was reoccupied by Government troops. I was just finishing my last lecture of the afternoon when I heard the sound of heavy English-type soldiers' boots running down the road between the compounds to the area around the hospital, the nurses' home, and the White House. Dismissing my class, I hurried out. Then I found the insurgents taking up positions behind the natural defenses on our hilltop which the Japanese Imperial Army used to occupy. This was the first time they had come on our property armed. They even had a Bren gun, which they were setting up beneath the biggest banyan tree. When I saw this, my glands pumped me so full of adrenalin that I was trembling all over with anger. But the highest-ranking man I could find was a sergeant, and he pretended he didn't know Burmese when I protested against their actions. He knew Burmese, all right; twenty minutes later he was speaking it fluently to me.

This is when I made a big mistake. I thought the Army was still the other side of Namkham and that I had plenty of time to go through channels. Locating Ba Saw, I ordered him to go to the rebel officer at the bungalow and tell him he was breaking international law by posting his men on hospital property and that if he did not remove them at once, the Army would be perfectly justified in firing on the hospital. Ba Saw ran off through the woods, and I went up to the hospital office to make sure all our administrative work was done for the day. When I came down fifteen minutes later, Ba Saw was returning on the run, reporting breathlessly that orders were being issued for the soldiers to withdraw from our land at once. I was completely mollified and continued on to the little house where I was staying.

I had just passed the White House when that sergeant who a few minutes before did not know Burmese ran up, gestured towards the south, and told me in Burmese that if I did not want them to open fire on the Army I had better run down and warn the Army not to continue coming up the valley. I was so sure the Army would not use the hospital as a shield that I lost three minutes trying to locate the Army in the valley. But they were not in the valley; they were almost at my feet, not a hundred yards away, traveling in single file along the stream at the foot of the hill.

There was no time to send a younger man; there was no time to spend arguing with the insurgents; there was no time even to make a white flag. I started down that steep hill as fast as my stiff knees would carry me. Then, when I was exactly halfway between the two lines, the confounded insurgents opened fire with all they had—Sten guns, carbines, and rifles. I was so overwhelmingly angry I wanted to die. I just stopped in my tracks and stood there, nicely outlined in my white clothes. The company of loyal Kachin soldiers was right in the open, the men in single file, a yard apart. The rebel Kachins were not just ordinary Kachins; they were deserters from a crack Kachin battalion. Some were using blanks, as was demonstrated to me by the Brigadier next morning. Some were using live ammunition, because one loyal soldier had a bullet pierce the skin of his leg and stop in the skin—in other words, a ricochet or a spent bullet. Not one of those sitting ducks was killed, and not another wounded. It is hard to believe that the rebels were shooting to kill.

At the volley the loyal Kachins dropped behind the bank of the little stream and returned fire for about fifteen minutes, although the insurgents had disappeared on the run after their first volley. The Army was most definitely using live ammunition. The lead spattered all around me, and I was soon covered with dirt. After a full minute of waiting to be shot, my anger at the insurgents cooled a bit. I decided I still had a few responsibilities to the hospital and nurses' training school, so I lay down gently in full view of the Army. When the soldiers finally started up the hill in skirmish formation I stood up and walked back up the hill while the soldiers continued to fire as they crossed our land towards the rebels' headquarters.

First I went into the little house, and found my sister, Wong Jack, the cook, and all the aunts, mothers, and four children hugging the floor by my bathroom door. One bullet had come through my south window and had ricocheted off the plastered stone walls. But no one was hurt. A mortar shell had struck through the roof of Grace's bedroom and had rather disarrayed her bed, much to the distress of a sick nurse who had taken refuge in the sitting room. At the nurses' home all the nurses were huddled in a small heap on the floor of the lower story, laughing with relief now that the Army was in control of the situation again. The walls of the Harper Memorial surgical block, around my office, and the walls of the maternity building were peppered with shots, but not a single patient had been hurt. The greatest damage was done to our water pipeline, which was full of bullet holes. As I had predicted, the nurses' home was not touched by a single bullet.

This sudden skirmish was over and no harm done—or no

physical harm. I couldn't know then how it would be magnified and distorted. For, amazing as it seemed to me, the charge was brought against me that I *allowed* the insurgents to take up the defensive positions in the hospital compound from which they opened fire on the Government troops.

As I made hurried rounds through each building to make sure no armed insurgent was using the hospital for a fort, one thing delighted me. Every single nurse on the early night shift, which had just gone on duty, had obeyed orders and had put all their patients down on the floor. In the gynecological ward the operative cases were in too serious condition to be put down on the floor. Two Karen girls were on duty there. If anyone had reason to fear being killed it was those two Karen girls. Yet I found them moving about in full view, from one patient to another, reassuring them and caring for their needs. Grandma Naomi, a Taungthu, was in charge.

That night a captain came and told me the Army was out of gas. So we dug up a drumful to help out. A lieutenant ordered me to evacuate all the late night-shift nurses and their baggage from Grace's house so that the men of his mortar battery could bivouac there. This I was delighted to do. But I was not delighted when they set up four mortars between Grace's house and my bedroom and fired sporadically for hours. The rebels had given the Army a right to shoot up the hospital by taking up positions around it. Now the Army was inviting the rebels to retaliate by doing the same thing.

That night I discovered that Dr. Ba Saw had disappeared. I have never seen him since. I will never understand what happened, what went on in his mind. He had obtained permission to go to Taunggyi in accordance with his original plan; but he had not gone there. If he had determined to rebel against the Government, one would think he would have joined the rebels at once. But he did not do so. For days after their arrival he performed all his numerous duties in the hospital, including his surgery, his ward work, and the night rounds. When the Commissioner urgently requested his services in Kutkai he went at once. At Kutkai he had found a box of his which had gone astray on his trip to Namkham from Rangoon. It contained surgical instruments given him by friends in America and some laboratory equipment for the Louisville-trained nurses. If he had intended to rebel, surely he would have turned those things over to the rebels. He did no such thing. He brought them to Namkham and turned them over to Naomi. When he returned from Kutkai he was still his old self, sharing my worries about the welfare of the nurses. When I ordered him to run to the insurgent commander and demand that his troops be taken off our land he was just finishing his evening ward rounds. There was still not the slightest evidence that he intended to go into open rebellion.

Then the firing broke out and he disappeared, leaving everything, even his clothes, behind.

What happened? I do not know. Perhaps he might have had a sudden funk. But during the war he had been shot at time and again and had never turned a hair.

I have never seen him since, and I have no idea whether he is alive or dead. Every once in a while a rumor drifts in. In 1952 some Chinese Communists were passing through Namkham, and one of them started to talk about Ba Saw helping the Chinese Communists in Paoshan. I had thought these Chinese were legitimate. As soon as I found that they were Communists I drove them out of the hospital. I wouldn't believe the word of a Communist of any race if he pointed to a piece of white cloth and told me it was white. If a Communist said it was white I would know it was really black and that my eyes were deceiving me.

I knew Ba Saw well. Soon after I had left him in America the Burmese Communist rebellion had broken out. His next letter to me was a wail of anguish: What would Americans think, now they knew there were enough Communists in Burma to start a rebellion? When he heard of the Karen rebellion in which his brother-in-law had been killed while trying to keep his men loyal to the Government, his reaction was that of a man profoundly hurt and unhappy. If he is now really a rebel at heart or a Communist he must have been subjected to some severe brain-washing somewhere. I cannot bear the thought that this man's services have been lost to Burma.

While the Army was chasing Naw Seng and his rebels all over the hills during these last months of 1949, Dr. Tu was suddenly taken sick with the type of influenza-pneumonia of which I had seen so much in 1918. In thirty-six hours he was dead. My two best doctors, surgeons of real skill, men who could keep this hospital serving most efficiently whether I lived or died, were lost to me and to Burma within six weeks of each other. There was little I could find to smile about.

Later I was criticized by a Kachin colonel who assisted in recapturing North Hsenwi State because I had not run away when I heard there was a possibility that the rebels might come to Namkham. My reasons are these: In the first place, I am an American and an ex-officer of the U. S. Army. I don't run very easily, especially if there is a bare possibility that I can help save anything out of chaos.

In the second place, I had a job. So far as the hospital was concerned, I was a private citizen. But I was an unpaid semiofficial Government servant so far as three-quarters of the nurses' training school was concerned. Now, if Communist China were to make an armed attack and the Burmese Army were to retreat, I would retreat with the Burmese Army on foot, if necessary. I would abandon every bit of equipment we could not take along, just as I had once done with General Stilwell. And I would use every single nurse and orderly I could persuade to follow me in serving the Burmese Army. With Nationalist Chinese I would not run but would stick out my chest and dare the Chinese to do their worst, as I had so often had to do from Pearl Harbor to V-J Day. But, with Karen-Kachin or even Burmese rebels, running would be a horrible mistake. It would result in the useless looting of the entire hospital. The people of Burma are a considerable improvement, even when in rebellion, over Chinese Nationalists, and they are a thousand times better than Chinese Communists.

Furthermore I had two hundred nurses in training—most of them Government-sponsored. If I stuck to my job the girls would not panic. If I ran they *would* panic, and be easy picking for any and every male they encountered. There was no possible way to transfer them all by truck somewhere, and if that had been possible, then to what place could I have taken them?

This first time the rebels came there were State and Union officials all around me. They did not inform me authoritatively that the rebels were coming—although they knew—and not one of them ordered me to evacuate personnel or abandon the hospital to looting. On the contrary, on this first occasion, State officials informed me that a legitimate conference was about to take place.

Lastly, the picture of these rebellions had long since come into focus. The multicolored insurgents would look for an important place where the Government was not in a position to withstand them. Then they would move in, and the Government would move out. While the rebels are in position they murder, loot, rape, commit arson and mayhem in proportion to the redness of the ideology they profess to adhere to. While this was going on, the Government would regroup, and then attack and drive the rebels out.

14

More Trouble

AFTER THE storming of the hospital and a night made sleep-
less by the mortars banging away outside my bedroom window I must have looked like a man with the grandfather of
all hangovers. I sent for three Kachin nurses whose relatives
were in the Army and asked them to let me know as soon
as the commanding officers of the Government troops came.
Instead of notifying me they brought them to the house.

I knew the second in command. He was Colonel Hkun
Nawng, who had married one of my first ten nurses. He was
the elder brother of Major Shan Lome, Chief Secretary of
the Kachin State Government, and of Saya Zow Yaw, who
runs the Kachin Baptist Seminary in Kutkai. I knew his
father before him. I did not know who his boss was, and I
certainly was unaware that he was the Brigadier Lazum
Tang who had recaptured Maymyo. If he had been wearing
his nice red flaps in his lapels that day I would have called
him General. If you err you should err on the right side. As
it was, I did not know his rank, so I did not call him anything. I started to talk, as usual. I told them that since the
insurgents had opened fire first, the Government troops had
been perfectly entitled to return fire and storm the hospital.
But, in using the hospital as a fort and setting up their
mortar battery on our hill, they were putting the insurgents

in a position to retaliate, and that would undoubtedly hurt nurses and patients of their own race, let alone other Burmese. I said I would appreciate it if they would withdraw their troops from our land.

The Brigadier's answer was to pull out a copy of his orders from Rangoon. Why he did this I shall never know, unless he wanted me to realize that he, and not the Government, should be blamed for anything that went wrong at Namkham. His orders were very specific. Under no circumstances was he to fire on a hospital or a mission. At Namkham he was doing both.

I pointed out that I was just asking him to obey his written orders. Then he objected to immediate withdrawal because his men were cooking their food all over our compounds. That was all right with me. I was in no hurry to get rid of the Army. My delight at having the Army back again and in control of the situation was as great as that of the youngest pupil nurse.

After the officers left me, I rang the bell for our regular chapel service. We have one every morning, and every nurse who has a mind to attend comes. On that morning I gave out the number of an English hymn, we read a chapter from the Bible in Burmese, a Kachin nurse prayed in Kachin, and we finished off with the Lord's Prayer in Burmese as usual. There was so much heartfelt gratitude that day that the White House was packed.

My next trouble was caused at our branch dispensary at Selan, twelve miles away. The municipal committee there had never felt responsibility for the welfare of the nurses, and nobody in the village took them into their homes. When the insurgents retreated, a Karen ordered the two girls, a

Kachin and a Shan, to board a jeep. He threw in all the drugs he could find and drove off with them. The Kachin girl, with innate courage, waited her time, escaped when the jeep was parked momentarily beside a convenient tree, and found her way back over thirty miles of mountain paths to Namkham. The Shan girl stayed with the insurgents until they abandoned the jeep beyond Kutkai, and then she was brought back by a Government official. Later she joined the insurgents, her lover being among them, and as far as I know, is with them still.

This first insurrection limited still more our work at Namkham. Ever since I first came there we had sent obstetrical teams or medical teams all over the nearby mountains and across the river into China whenever urgent calls came in. But with the insurgents reported to be scattered all over our own mountains we stopped sending out teams. The Palaungs and Kachins did not like this a bit. For a while, with the Brigadier's permission, we sent a few teams to villages in China, but soon the insurgents crossed the border, and Communism began to take over China. That put a stop to all our outside work except in the plain on our side of the river. If Shans and Kachins in China will carry their patients to the Ledo Road we will send out to bring them to the hospital and then promptly have them screened by the proper authorities. We take no chances with any Communist, and not one of our staff is allowed by me to set foot in Communist China, not even to save the lives of the long-suffering Shans and Kachins beyond the Bamboo Curtain. Since there have been no insurgents on our side of the line since the beginning of 1952, teams now go up into the mountains occasionally—unless Chinese Nationalists are raiding the country—but usually the patients are carried down to us.

Christmas of 1949 was dismal. We had our usual big Christmas dinner with the school, up on the baseball ground. A number of local officials and police were present as our guests. It is still a mystery to me why I was not told that Naw Seng was expected momentarily and that they were evacuating with all the Army to Muse to defend the great American-built airfield there. If I had had that information, while I could not have evacuated and left the hospital for Naw Seng to loot, I could at least have buried our drugs and surgical supplies, just as we had buried our gasoline drums before his first visit. But before I knew anything about the evacuation, Naw Seng had already fought a small battle at Selan and had cut us off effectively from Muse. The next thing I knew, there he was again, under our banyan trees, with several vehicles which he had commandeered and about twenty soldiers.

When he drove up and started shouting, I was giving my morning lectures. Thinking it must be the Army, I went to the front door. Then I recognized Naw Seng. I went out to argue with him. Half of his men were already taking up positions on our land.

As I approached, the rest of his men surrounded me with Sten guns, carbines and rifles at the ready. I am not what anyone would call a brave man. No person as scared as I am of harmless snakes could possibly be considered brave. But when people pull guns on me, my adrenal glands begin to act so powerfully that in a second I am in a towering rage and I don't bother to think about my own safety. But my mind is quicker than ever with regard to my other responsibilities.

"You talk glibly about your fight for the betterment of the Kachins," I said. "Now look what you've done. The last time you were here your men took up positions on our land, and the Government troops had to storm the hospital. Because of that you almost destroyed the institution that has been working harder than any other for the welfare of the Kachins. Get your men off this land!"

"I want Doctor Ba Saw's surgical instruments and this list of medicines," he said.

"I'll give you his instruments and such medicines as we can spare if you will swear to get off this land with your men and stay off."

"I swear," he said.

I was anxious lest he should follow me into the hospital and get a look into our medical and surgical storerooms. While my mind was racing in search of a pretext to keep him out, he himself furnished me with one.

"Is the Selan Myosa a patient in your hospital?" he asked. For some reason he had a personal feud with the Selan Myosa.

"Not as far as I know," I answered. "He is certainly not in the surgical building."

I knew the Myosa was not in the hospital, but this was the best gag I could think up. Then I noticed Dr. Roy about twenty yards away.

"But you had better look for yourself. Dr. Roy will take you through the medical building."

Roy got the idea at once. He kept Naw Seng busy for a long time, and his bodyguard went with him. I hurried into the surgical block, found Grandma Naomi, and had her hustle Ba Saw's instruments into one small box and a few medicines that we would not miss into another small box.

Then I sent Ai Sai, our hospital orderly, with the two boxes over to the White House, where Naw Seng's men were guarding his commandeered vehicles. By this time he was in the surgical block, casting his eye longingly at the power unit that ran our X-ray. If it had not been so heavy he probably would have run off with it. By talking feverishly I managed to keep him from seeing the blocked doors of the storerooms. Finally I reminded him again of his having sworn to leave us alone, and then at last he departed.

The yielding up of the surgical instruments and medicine to Naw Seng—done only to prevent his making off with our valuable stores of drugs and supplies—became the basis for the third and most serious of the charges against me when I was arrested.

In those days we had three eight-hour shifts. That gave the nurses a chance to bathe, dress up in their prettiest, and go for a paradelike stroll along the main road. If they had money they stopped for a snack in our local restaurants. Apparently five Karen girls, one of them the granddaughter of the Karenni chief U Bee, who had first started the quarrel between the Baptists and Catholics in Karenni State, stopped several times in one of these restaurants and listened to Naw Seng's blandishments. At noon on New Year's Day they all disappeared, bag and baggage. I found out about it at six o'clock while I was getting dressed for our New Year's Day dinner. A Karen nurse brought me a letter left behind by one of the five. She bade me goodbye and regretted that they had had to leave without my permission. I did not enjoy that dinner.

The next day Emily reported that two Kachin seniors

had taken to the woods because Naw Seng had made all
sorts of vile threats of what he would do to them if they
didn't join his insurgents. I asked her to send the girls to
me as soon as she could find them. Find them she did, in
a far corner of the nurses' trunk room in the attic, cowering
under the eaves.

"You did wrong to run away," I said. "That just postpones
trouble. Naw Seng swore he would leave us alone. The
thing for you to do is to tell him straight out that you are
not joining him."

"We will, if we can do so when you're with us," they
replied.

So I sent for Naw Seng. This was the only time I ever
did send for him. Strange to say, he came up to the little
house, at dusk.

"You swore you would leave us alone if I gave you those
medicines and instruments," I said angrily. "Now look
what you've done. You've enticed five Karens to join you,
and now you're passing out threats to Kachin girls if they
don't join you too. You've broken your promise."

"I just want to talk to the Kachin girls," he said.

"You can talk to them in my presence but only on condition that you will stop talking to them behind my back."

"It's a deal!"

I sent for all the Kachin nurses. They filed into my dining
room and stood silently. Naw Seng made them quite a
speech, using the Kachin language. I do not speak Kachin,
but I have heard so many Kachin sermons that it is possible
for me not only to get the gist of a speech but to recognize
good Kachin when I hear it. Naw Seng missed his calling.
He should have been a preacher. His language was very good.
I managed to keep track of all the "facts" he was presenting

so that if any Kachin nurse seemed unduly impressed I could contradict them later. All the while I was fascinated, watching the insane glitter of his eyes. His speech was full of ideas of grandeur.

Briefly he outlined his complaints against the Government—the things which had first led him to rebel and join the insurgents. He went into detail about his capture of Maymyo and Mandalay. This was the first time I knew that he had been in command of that expedition. He lost me completely when he talked about his finding of "Operation Aung San" and his interpretation of it. I had to ask one of our senior girls to translate that part later. He skipped completely any mention of his arrogance at Thazi-Meiktila which had kept him from his rendezvous with the Karens at Toungoo. He was full of abuse of the Kachins who had foiled his noble aspirations at the conference in Namkham in September.

Then he ended with prayer!

The nurses filed out silently, all but the two senior Kachins whom he had tried to coerce into joining him.

"Say what you have to say," I ordered.

"We are not going to join you," said the girls.

Only two more nurses decamped. They were girls who had been intending to join him for some time, girls with sweethearts among the insurgents. One of them had made trouble for us for years and had been disciplined again and again. In fact, I had once suspended her from school for a year and then taken her back on her father's intercession. Her father and her two older sisters were real people. Someone had informed her father that she had treasonable ideas, and he had come down and ordered her not to join the insurgents. When I found out about this I sent for her and gave her a half-hour's harangue, telling her to behave herself and not to shame her family as well as herself. An hour after she left me she disappeared.

That girl couldn't be loyal to anything or anyone. I later heard that she married her insurgent. She stayed with the insurgents for about three months until her husband was killed in a battle with Government troops. Then she abandoned them and came back into Government-held territory with complete immunity. The next time I saw her, she had bobbed her hair Chinese-style, had acquired a permanent wave, and was traveling all over the Shan and Kachin States wearing enough lipstick, rouge, and powder to supply an American woman for a week.

Probably because he could not get any co-operation from me, Naw Seng ceased to trouble us and soon disappeared. He must have left behind about a company of Kachin villagers whom he had been recruiting for months from backwoods villages. This land of ours is such a natural fort that twice I caught squads of his men sneaking in after dark and trying to dig in. On both occasions I sent for high-caliber Kachin nurses who by nature could speak in a tone of authority, and we soon drove them out.

When Brigadier Lazum Tang finally decided to return and recapture Namkham for the second time, he ordered a company of his men to make a frontal attack on the hospital in skirmish formation. We all knew that there was no insurgent within miles, and the nurses joined me in furnishing a grandstand for the play. It was as good as a movie. By the time the Brigadier had been informed that the coast was entirely clear and was driving up the hill in a jeep with a ten-foot flagpole and a flag of Burma as big as his jeep, we were entirely prepared with a welcoming committee to meet him.

Perhaps it was mere bad luck, but I always seemed to meet Brigadier Lazum Tang with a reproach on my lips. This time I was so indiscreet as to tell him that if he had not abandoned us to the enemy, we would not have been forced to give those instruments and medicines to Naw Seng. Also that Naw Seng would not then have been able to induce seven of our nurses to join him.

From that time until January 30, 1950, the Brigadier and the civilian officials who returned to administer the area ignored me completely. Without asking permission, they took charge. They ordered various groups of nurses to stop duty at all hours and go to their headquarters to be quizzed about my sins. Luckily the three little trouble-makers were no longer with us. The girls who were ordered to testify undoubtedly told the truth, or more lies would have been sprung on me, later, than were.

On January 30, 1950, the nurses in training were given eighteen hours to prepare to leave Namkham the following morning. Aside from the Karen girls, who said they would leave only if placed under arrest, not one was allowed to remain.

The official who thus broke up the training school on his own initiative guaranteed that on presentation of bills the Government would immediately pay us the moneys which had been due us for some months. Grace and I borrowed all the savings of the staff nurses, paid all the amounts due to the pupil-nurses, stayed up all night to get all the papers in order, handed them to the official before he left town, and then waited six months before this promise was kept and the money was repaid to us.

About two days after the official dissolution of the training school, the Karen pupil-nurses who had been permitted to remain sent me a petition begging me to guarantee their actions as I had the actions of the Karen men on our staff. Grace and I sent for the girls and said that five of their number had turned traitor without our knowledge. We had no reason to trust them and would give no guarantee to the Government unless each one of them gave us on the Bible her solemn written oath of allegiance to the Government. The Government respected my guarantee and left the girls in our charge. We continued the training of these girls during the difficult months that followed, although our training school had been disrecognized. Classes went on as usual, and as a result our training school never ceased to exist on a private basis.

As work became available for them in other hospitals the Government informed the girls who had been on Government scholarships and they left gladly to fulfill their duties to their Government. Four of them married loyal army officers. Later one went insane from grief, and I had to use insulin shock therapy before I could send her and two others, whose home areas had been freed of insurgents, back to Karenni. One is now nursing in a mission hospital in the loyal part of Karenni, her mother having died of exposure during the insurrection. Three, who still know nothing about their parents, are on our staff now.

Nothing nice happened during the next months except the arrival from the United States of five thousand dollars' worth of gift drugs and an alcohol still given to me by Seagram's, in Louisville. Grace went to Rangoon and at length obtained permission from the Union Government, the Shan State Government, and the Army to transport these articles by plane to the Muse airfield. The only times during those depressing months that I moved off our hospital hill was when I went twice on Government orders to Muse to take receipt of the medicines and the still. There were few patients because the roads were blocked and because people at a distance thought that when the nursing school was closed the hospital also had been closed.

15

Arrest

WHENEVER I start dreaming about snakes it is a sure sign that something bad is going to happen to me. By August of 1950 not only was I dreaming of snakes, I was seeing them as well. While toweling myself after a bath I saw something move outside the bathroom window. It was a huge snake. I stuck my head through the bathroom door and yelled to Wong Jack in the kitchen. But by the time he got there the snake had disappeared. At dinner Wong Jack had an evil glitter in his eye. He sniffed at me suspiciously, but he well knew I did not have a drop of alcohol in the house.

Then I was wakened from an afternoon siesta by a pounding on the bedroom window. At first I thought it was a nurse trying to arouse me for an emergency. But I was wrong. It was another snake, which had climbed up the pumelo tree there and was trying to get in.

Then on the seventh of August I came back from the hospital and found Wong Jack had just killed a six-foot cobra outside the dining room. He gave us a good dinner that night, for his faith in me had been restored. But my faith had not revived at all. I still had that sick feeling of anticipation of serious trouble.

On the evening of the fourteenth a staff nurse came running from a house about a hundred yards away. They had treed a cobra, she said, near the roof of the chicken coop beside the headmaster's house. The snake was in such a position that they could not reach it with a club or with the short swordlike *dah* the Burmese use. Would I please bring my shotgun and shoot it?

I was skeptical of its really being a cobra, so I went up to look. It was a cobra, all right, as thick as my arm, twisted around the top of a post near the thatch roof, with its head poised on its beautiful hooded neck as it watched me. Weak-kneed, I hurried for my gun, located my last two twelve-bore cartridges, and shot that hood to pieces. If I had realized the importance of all these omens I would have dug a hole just big enough for me to drop into and pull the hole back in on top of me.

The next morning when Grace and I were finishing coffee a lot of Kachin soldiers surrounded my house. Wong Jack came and told me that two officers wanted to speak to me. I went to the back door.

"Yes, gentlemen?"

"We are going to search your house."

"What for?"

"Evidence of treason."

"You have a warrant, of course?"

They handed me a much-signed-and-sealed order to the effect that since the undersigned judge had had convincing proof presented to him that I had been engaged in treason, etc., etc.

I opened the door wide.

"Come in, gentlemen, and make yourselves at home."

One of the officers was an inspector of the Criminal Intelligence Department. He made himself at home. The other

outranked him. He was a superintendent in Special Branch
II, the branch of the police which deals with foreigners.
He never did feel at home. He was so embarrassed at the
task assigned him that he just fidgeted around, keeping his
eye on the Inspector to see he did nothing unlawful.

The Inspector's suspicions were immediately aroused by
my shotgun leaning against the fireplace in the dining room
where I had left it for Wong Jack to clean. He was sur-
prised to find it unloaded. Then his suspicions returned as
he sniffed it and discovered that it had been fired very
recently. I told him about the snake, but he was not convinced. I offered to have the snake dug up for his inspection, but he was still unconvinced.

He went carefully through all the personal letters on
my desk, letters from the family and the letters from the
nurses who had been forced to leave in January. He thumbed
through all my ex-Army pocket books.

He climbed up into the attic, which is not an attic at
all—just a heat-insulation space between the roof and the
ceiling. I was relieved when he did not fall through. Then
he searched the De Soto. Before he was finished he had
wasted about two hours.

"All right," he said, "let's go!"

"Where to?"

"Central Jail in Rangoon."

"I suppose you have another warrant?"

A second warrant was then produced. This ordered my
arrest under Section Five of the Public Order Preservation
Act, which entitled the Government to arrest and jail anyone on suspicion without having to produce them for trial.
So many people had been thrown into jail under it in 1948,

1949, and 1950 that one Rangoon newspaper printed an allegory about the fat, country man-eating tiger who asked his city cousin why he was all skin and bones. The city tiger, with tears in his eyes, replied that so many people had been thrown into jail under this Act that there was no one left to walk the streets on whom he could make a meal. Yet even the victims recognized that in a country like Burma in those days such a law was needed for people who were really under suspicion. What they resented was that apparently the law was sometimes used for personal enemies.

"Your search warrant orders you to search every place I have access to," I reminded the Inspector. "You haven't even been to my office yet."

"Where's that?"

"Over in the hospital."

I led him over. As before, the Inspector put on a big act with a lot of old letters from America which had lain unanswered on my desk for more than a year because we had had no regular mail service. Meanwhile Pansy Po, my secretary, had opened up all our locked files and spread them out for inspection. Without looking at them the Inspector started to leave. I spoke up.

"If, as I suspect, your charges of treason are based on last year's occupations by the insurgents, you will find all the evidence, pro and con, in those files."

"Haven't got time."

"Your orders are to search every place to which I have access," I reminded him again, "and now when you get to the place where the evidence really is, you won't look."

"Haven't got time."

"There is evidence in there that I have never been guilty

of any seditious activity. You have no right not to look."

"Haven't time. I'll give you half an hour to get a bed roll and a bag packed."

"O.K., you boys are making history."

They gave me no time to say goodbye to anyone but my sister Grace and the three nurses who were helping me pack. There was no chance to show Grace the surgical patients or to leave instructions for their welfare. She was no surgeon, and I knew that the surgical cases would be her greatest burden.

Grace was so appalled by what was taking place that she could do nothing but stand by until the officers were ready to take me away. Then she spoke with great determination.

"Don't worry, Gordon, I will keep this hospital open and doing its duty for the people of the country until you are cleared of all charges and allowed to return to Namkham, if I die doing it."

She kept that promise very literally. I never saw her again.

But I did stop and ask two Kachin Army captains who were patients if they thought their colonel would let them assign a squad to keep the hospital from being looted.

"Rest easy," they said. "We'll assign the squad, and the colonel will give his wholehearted approval."

This satisfied me.

The ranking officer gave me the best seat in the jeep while he sat, most uncomfortably, between me and the driver. The Inspector and two embarrassed Kachin soldiers sat in behind where they were not comfortable but where the Inspector was quite safe. To my astonishment they did not shackle me as they had a perfect right to do when the charge was treason. As it turned out, they were probably playing safe.

As we were driving to Muse the first feeling to overwhelm me was shame—shame at the idea of anyone believing for a moment that I could be guilty of treason to Burma, let alone arresting me. In the oriental languages that was a terrific loss of face. In the American language I did not know where to look, and for at least five miles I hoped none of the thousands of people in the valley who loved me would see my shame. Then I turned back into an American again. If a man is big in any way he cannot lose face! This thought made me feel better and my chin went up.

At Muse, eighteen miles away, we stopped for lunch. Some women who had been patients recognized me and came up to speak. When they saw the Inspector, they turned and ran. A lot of the Muse bigshots saw me and wanted to know what the blazes was going on.

"I am going to jail in Rangoon," I said.

"What on earth for?"

"Treason."

"Treason? You?"

"Yes. Me."

"Somebody has a screw loose. Well, come and have some tea with us."

They drove like mad from Muse to Kutkai, an extra jeep-load of soldiers spreading out with their guns at the ready whenever there was a stop. After passing Kutkai, the last Kachin town, eighty miles from Namkham, the two officers began to breathe more easily. When we reached Hsenwi, the first Shan town, they told their driver he could take his time.

"Before we reached Kutkai we were afraid of an ambush in which you might have been hurt. We are responsible for your safety," the Inspector explained.

At Lashio they took me to the Officers' Club. If I had wanted to escape I could easily have done it the two nights we waited there for the plane. The jeep driver told Dr. Ai Lun, a boy whom I had helped through High School and Medical School, that I was under arrest in the officers' mess, and he came up the next morning to pay his respects. There he was told by the Inspector that he had been misinformed —Dr. Seagrave was not in Lashio. Later Ai Lun taxed the driver with having given him false information.

"I didn't lie to you," said the driver. "The Inspector did. Dr. Seagrave was there. They were keeping him out of sight for fear that if the town found out about his arrest there would be an armed rescue."

Throughout four meals the two police officials had to listen to Kachin officers in the mess tell tall tales of wondrous cures I was alleged to have obtained operating on relatives and friends, and still more impossible stories of my prowess as a teacher of nurses. This was pitiful for them and embarrassing for me.

When we boarded the plane for Rangoon the Inspector put me in a seat beside an Englishwoman. She turned out to be the Superintendent of Nurses of the Burma Silver Mines Corporation at Namtu. She had suddenly resigned and was starting back to England. Several of our graduates worked in that hospital, one of them being the "Tugboat Annie" of *Burma Surgeon* and *Burma Surgeon Returns*. I had no idea that I was dynamiting a dam when I innocently asked if our girls were giving good service. The dam burst, and there was a torrent of words. The lady had held an im-

portant position in the Rangoon General Hospital, and
she thought she knew all about how to handle Burmese
nurses. But at Namtu her prewar type of discipline had
brought on a strike absolutely unique in her experience and
in mine, too, for that matter. The girls had gone on sick
strike. I do not mean that they goldbricked to stay off duty;
they went on duty, but they refused to follow the rules of
hygiene necessary to remain well, and when they became ill
they refused to take any treatment. They went on duty and
stayed there until they dropped. Tugboat had gone on duty
during an attack of pneumonia—an adaptation of the hunger strike.

I had an almost overwhelming desire to chuckle. Before
Independence a Westerner could drive Burmans around
with inflexible discipline and get away with it most of the
time if he had the British Government behind him. I never
could and I never wanted to. Even then you could get much
farther by leading than by driving. Since Independence only
the Burmans can occasionally drive Burmans, and even
then they have to have a good grip on short hair if they
want to succeed. Tugboat had been an excellent nurse with
us all through the war because I had her loyalty.

You have to spend at least one night in the Barr Street
lockup in Rangoon before you can be admitted to the rel-
atively palatial Central Jail. Indeed, one's experiences are
incomplete if one does not spend at least one night there.
And yet, for me it was comparatively de luxe. The jailer
turned out a lot of other prisoners from a ward and installed a wooden bed. I had brought a tin of DDT, and
while no one was looking, I scattered it all over the bed,
thereby keeping the total number of bites somewhere below

a hundred. Not all the phenol compounds they had used so freely could disguise the previous drenchings of urine, but being a doctor, I knew that the olfactory nerves would soon get tired, and the fragrance didn't worry me. What I disliked was a 200-watt bulb in the ceiling which could not be turned off, and the crowds that watched. Why do we Americans have these nervous systems? But I will hand it to my fellow prisoners and jailers. A lot of them were far too interested, but most of them were appalled at what was happening to a gray-haired American. Not one of them gloated.

16

Jail

NEXT DAY the Chief Jailer admitted me to the Central Jail as a provisional Class A prisoner, and sent me to a large ward occupied by only two other men, both lieutenant-colonels in the Burma Army—Anglo-Burmans who had been trained in the Army by the British. Both were in jail under suspicion and had then been in jail without trial for a year and a half. Col. Bill Hardless recognized me from his term of service in Muse in 1946 and merely gaped at me. Col. Wally Unger looked ferociously at the convict who was carrying in my stuff.

"What the unprintable does the Chief mean, sending in a stranger without first consulting with us?"

"I'm Dr. Seagrave of Namkham," I said.

"Dr. Seagrave? Good Lord! What are you in for?"

"High Treason."

Bill gaped wide than ever while Wally produced fully documented evidence that if profanity is the sign of a good soldier he should have been a five-star general. They moved all their own stuff around and gave me the best part of the ward. We soon had a men's club. Bill spent his days doing oil paintings, copying the pictures on the back of my *Time* magazines and reading the *Catholic Digest*. Wally tried to boss the two convicts we had for cooks. Soon we had a fourth member—Mr. Wiltshire, Deputy Commissioner of Katha District near Bhamo, who had repelled a Communist invasion of Katha and had been praised by the Prime Minister himself as "the type of officer we need all over Burma." Now he was taking the rap for some other men who were responsible for the theft of a million and a half rupees from the Katha Treasury while he had been saving the town and district from the Communists.

The lives of all four of us had overlapped frequently in the past, and our common friends were numerous. All four of us had a large repertoire of stories, some of which had a punch line only when told in Burmese. When we ran out of jokes, one of them would demand a lecture on some medical or surgical subject. It is fun to watch their eyes pop when you straighten out their fiction with properly documented truth.

As Class A prisoners we were allowed to buy newspapers. We took the Rangoon *Nation* and the *New Times of Burma*. The *Times* had the Associated Press dispatches. Its Burma coverage followed the majority party line and gave the Government's interpretation of day-to-day occurrences—a very desirable feature.

The *Nation*, on the other hand, is irrepressible. It preaches and practices, in the very best sense, free speech. It is critical of what it regards as mistaken Government policies, but not rabidly so. It gives credit where credit is due, and the credit is thereby greatly enhanced. In it was printed some of the most exquisite and subtle satire in the English language since Dean Swift. Some of the satire while I was in jail was so subtle that I am sure its victims regarded the articles as complimentary. I have heard it compared with *The Manchester Guardian*. On one occasion the editor heard a rumor that an order had been issued for his arrest. Thereupon, with tongue in cheek, he advertised for someone to take his place as editor while he did a term in jail. He was not jailed, of course. It was just another of those delightful rumors. Finally, in order to get into jail, he asked the jail authorities to lock him up for a day so he could find out how it felt and do a series of articles on jail life. With policies like these, the *Nation* has the largest circulation of any English-language newspaper in Burma. That is what real democracy means. A democratic government permits criticism.

In jail I had plenty of time to go over the circumstances which had apparently caused my arrest, and for a while I was both bitter and disillusioned. So far as I could see, my real troubles had begun when the Karen rebels had been reported coming north from Taunggyi in the late summer of 1949. This had been a little less than a year before my arrest. While I was suspicious of their motives, no efforts to stop them had been made by the Burma Army. Then as they came north of Lashio, the garrison battalion, which could have stopped them with almost no casualties near Kutkai, had withdrawn through Namkham just as if no insurrection existed. When these rebels did reach Namkham they had been accompanied by two Government officials whom I had trusted. Then other Government officials whom I knew had come up from Bhamo to have meetings with the insurgents.

These meetings made everything seem legal until suddenly and without warning all the Government officials disappeared and left me surrounded by rebels. It had seemed to me that I should use such influence as I had to protect many Burmese civilians who had taken refuge with me and to keep two hundred Government-sponsored pupil-nurses under my care from stampeding. If I had run, leaving the nurses to be raped and the hospital to be looted, apparently I would have incurred no suspicion. But I had a different idea of my responsibility to the Government, so I had stayed on and accomplished my job. The civilians and nurses were left unmolested, and the hospital was not looted; but very grave accusations had been made against me in Rangoon.

I finally came to see that my worst mistake had been not to realize that the Burmese Government had some reason to be suspicious of foreigners. At least two Britishers had been admittedly guilty of High Treason against Burma. I understand now that the Government of Burma could have hanged one of them, but nevertheless it had generously permitted him to deport himself from Burma. The other is said to have joined a group of rebels and to have been later killed in a pitched battle. Several American Baptist missionaries had also been indiscreet. Completely absorbed in my medical and surgical work, I had hardly noticed what these men had done. The result was that when some three or four officials who did not know me very well were rumored in late 1949 and early 1950 to be out after my scalp, I paid little attention, feeling that this was just another of those things that would blow over. Instead of taking this attitude and trying to forget the whole matter, I should, for my own position, have set about securing and listing witnesses of my innocence and taking sworn statements from them.

My most severe anguish, however, was caused by my worry about the future of the hospital at Namkham. For twenty years before World War II I had built up that hospital and its practice, convinced that I was accomplishing something there that was really worth while. The Japanese

and the United States Air Force had destroyed that hospital
and that practice. But both had been more than restored
before the rebellion hit Namkham in 1949 and brought
destruction in its wake. The only doctor left in Namkham
when I was arrested was my sister Grace, and she was not a
surgeon. Nor was a hospital on the China border any task for
an unaided woman. Grace had promised me after my arrest
that she would keep that hospital open until I was freed
or she would die trying. I was desperately fearful not only
that the hospital would cease to exist but also that Grace
might really kill herself keeping it open. My fear for her was
tragically fulfilled.

I soon learned that the United States Embassy had assigned an aide to assist me. On his first visit he asked me if
I wanted a lawyer. I said that of course I did, but I could
not afford first-class counsel and was unwilling to have a
poor one. I had spent all my money on the hospital at Namkham and had been without a salary since January, 1946,
putting all my lecture fees into the hospital. True, I had
saved a fund for the security of my wife and children, but
this I refused to touch. In response to all this the aide said
that he had reason to believe that several of the best lawyers
in Burma would be delighted to take my case for a pittance
or for nothing.

The next day he returned with a list of four topnotch
lawyers. The first name was that of U Kyaw Myint, who,
the aide muttered in an undertone, had come to the embassy to talk about me. Now, U Kyaw Myint means "Uncle
Famous and High-minded." As soon as I learned that it was
the U Kyaw Myint—the younger brother of the assassinated
minister, U Tin Tut, and himself a former Justice of the

Supreme Court, I was wild with joy. U Kyaw Myint soon came to see me.

"Sir," I said, "I have no money except the life savings of my sisters Rachel and Grace, both of whom have turned their bank accounts over to me. But even that only totals a thousand dollars. I can't touch the money I have banked for my wife and children."

"Doctor, we won't talk about money—ever!" he replied. "As a Burman, I think I owe it to you."

Many Americans have asked me how to pronounce U Kyaw Myint's name. The "U" is pronounced "oo." This means "uncle" and is the "mister" or "monsieur" of Burma. The "Kyaw" is one syllable, and you never get the hard "K" quite right unless you can say something halfway between "chaw" and "jaw." The "Myint" is also one syllable and rhymes with "mint." Now try to soften that "M" up by putting a bit of "Y" after it, but still just one syllable, as thus: "M'yint." Now you have it—"Oo Jaw M'yint."

As a youngster, U Kyaw Myint had stopped school to take a job as a clerk to an official of a great timber company. He traveled all over the country with this gentleman and his wife. Since they knew no Burmese at all, in talking with them and doing a great deal of pecking at typewriters with two fingers, he picked up his very excellent knowledge of the English language. When World War I broke out, he left school and joined the British Army, becoming a junior officer. At the end of that war he studied law in London at the Middle Temple and was admitted to the bar in 1923. In the mid-twenties he was the first Burman to become a member of the constituent assembly at Delhi, Burma at that time being part of India.

U Kyaw Myint comes from a distinctly upper-class Burmese family which is as proud of its family inheritance and as determined to maintain its family integrity as any old "county" family in England. There were four brothers, U Kyaw Myint being the second. The eldest was the great U Tin Tut, a high-ranking Indian Civil Service officer in British times and by all accounts the most experienced minister in the provisional government set up by General Aung San and taken over by U Nu after the General's assassination.

All that time U Kyaw Myint was a Justice of the Supreme Court. It was he who was assigned to set up the Special Tribunal, with himself as President, to try prewar prime minister U Saw and his accomplices for the mass slaying of General Aung San and the members of his cabinet in 1947. Later U Kyaw Myint resigned his Supreme Court seat and went back into the private practice of law, much to my future benefit.

The third brother, U Myint Thein, was the Burmese Ambassador to Peiping and in 1953 presented Burma's case against the Chinese Nationalists in Burma to the United Nations. The world should hear much of him in the future. The youngest brother, U Htin Aung, is now Rector or President, to use the parallel American title, of the University of Rangoon.

Compared with other Burmese U Kyaw Myint is neither large nor small, but he at once gives you the impression of being big, in every sense of the word. It is only when I am actually standing beside him that I realize that instead of being a couple of inches taller, he is actually an inch shorter than I.

He is an extremely handsome man, with two physical characteristics which, since they make him so very effective in court, I'll wager he could well have developed after hours of practice in front of a mirror. He has a delightfully wry smile. This becomes positively lopsided when his opponent is making more of an ass of himself than usual, but at the same time it is a smile which greatly encourages his clients. It conveys the meaning that nobody is going to coerce him or put anything over on his client. His second characteristic is a very slight cast to his eye, which makes him a holy terror to any witnesses who think they can lie to him. One eye looks directly into your face and the other directly into your soul.

On this first visit to me in the jail, U Kyaw Myint informed me that the embassy had been told that if I would leave the country, I would not be prosecuted.* I refused instantly. I am no quitter. I was not guilty of any treason, and I was not willing to give up my life work for this country without a fight. Furthermore, I was quite certain that justice could still be had in Burma. Later, after I was dismissed under this first charge, this offer was repeated. Again I refused. I fully expected to be faced with false witnesses, but I still wonder if I would have been man enough to stand trial if I had had any conception of how perfectly foul lying testimony can be. During a treason trial one feels as if he were on top of a high pedestal, stripped completely naked, with atomic gamma rays exposing his innards to the world. When I refused to deport myself the cabinet is alleged to have argued in favor of deporting me, but the Prime Minister, U Nu—God bless him—objected.

* At the time of my trial, many friends were puzzled as to how I could be prosecuted for the crime of treason in Burma, since I did not owe allegiance to Burma but only to the United States. The definition of treason in Burma's High Treason Act, 1948, is devoid of any reference to allegiance. It differs thus from our own statute, which reads: "Any person or persons who, owing allegiance to the United States of America, shall," etc.

17

Imprisonment

ALL THE way down from Namkham I had been obliged to drink unboiled water. Hence, about five days after I became a guest of the Government in the Central Jail I came down with a new attack of amebic dysentery. I reported to the jail doctor, and with his consent began treating myself with the drugs I had brought with me for this very emergency.

I would soon have been all right if I had not developed an abscessed tooth. In Namkham I would promptly have gone over to the hospital, asked Grandma Naomi to put in a procaine block for me, and in nothing flat I would have extracted the offending member myself. Since the war I have extracted an average of one of my own teeth per year.

I reported again to the doctor, and he gave me some oil of cloves to hold me overnight. The next morning I asked the embassy aide to arrange for immediate attention by a dentist whom I knew to be the best in Burma. Day after day went by, and no dentist. After a week by which time eight teeth had become involved, I wanted to know what the reason for delay was, and I was informed innocently that private dentists and doctors could only be obtained by applying through the prison doctor to the Government, which process would ordinarily take two weeks. I put in formal application, and on the twelfth day of my misery the dentist showed up. He extracted three molars the first sitting, three incisors the next and two pre-molars the third.

By this time my morale was pretty low. No one knew just what kind of concrete charges the prosecuting attorney, the Assistant Attorney General of Burma, was going to bring against me. A year had gone by since the occupations of Namkham by the insurgents, during which time I had done my best to forget all disagreeable matters while doing as much constructive medical, surgical, and educational work as the military government of the Namkham area had permitted. This meant that I now had to dig into remote compartments of my brain, dust off a lot of disagreeable episodes, fit them together so as to be the truth, the whole truth, and nothing but the truth, so help me God. Then I had to write them all out in longhand and turn them over to my lawyer.

Had I been well, the time would have been unhappy enough. I have always suffered from an excess of thyroid secretion which drives me along very happily when I can work hard and fast and constructively but makes vacations from work impossible to tolerate. World War II had taught me a lot. But it had not taught me to enjoy inaction and certainly not inaction behind bars. The much-publicized jail reforms in Burma had not been instituted at that time. There were convicts with clubs bossing other convicts. There was a head warder who used his club quite freely unless the ordinary class of convicts somehow managed to smuggle in money to bribe him to leave them alone. The jail had a delightful habit of sending a warder around with a small crowbar which he would bang on every section of bar in every window or door to make sure that no one had been using a file or a hack saw. He always did this at the quietest and hottest time of the day when, if you were ill, you were doing your best to relax and sleep it off. Japanese war criminals were playing baseball or quoit tennis just outside the ward, emitting the most nerve-racking yells at every good or bad play. At night the night warders, scared to death as a result of a recent riot, used to sing at the top of their voices to keep up their courage. Or they would gather in groups near our ward and argue politics among themselves or with the Communists in the cells above us. One simply could not sleep. When my dysentery almost healed, I came down with an attack of the mild flu that was going around, and by the time that was under control my dysentery relapsed.

The food in the jail was not at all impossible. There was plenty to eat, especially for the Class A prisoners. The trouble was the cooks. We each of us had a convict batman. These boys knew nothing about cooking, but they did the best they could and as long as one was well the food was quite tolerable. But when you are nauseated from dysentery and your jowls ache and your gums are lacerated you need an expert French chef to be able to eat. The Chief Jailer laid himself out to be kind to me, giving me an occasional chicken and, when I was really ill, he detailed a warder, who had once cooked for an English family, to cook special meals for me.

Of our three batmen, one was a much older man. While he was in jail he kept dreaming about elephants. Every time he saw an elephant in his dreams someone in Class A was sure to be released inside of six weeks. The Colonels told me he had not once been wrong. We used to corner him every morning and inquire about his night's rest.

He dreamed about an elephant almost immediately after Mr. Wiltshire joined us, and sure enough, inside two weeks

Wiltshire went out on bail. Then he dreamed about another elephant and one of our batmen was released. Finally the night came when he dreamed about a white elephant and an oxcart. I claimed the white elephant was for me and the oxcart for him. Inside the six weeks' time limit his dream came true, for I was transferred. One thing worried him about the oxcart of his dream: It seemed to have wings, and he couldn't understand why the wings were there. When he was released, he didn't have a cent to his name, so he went to see an official who had served in his home town of Tavoy. The official put him on the next plane for Tavoy. The wings belonged in the dream, after all.

A few days after my arrival I wrote a note to my sister Grace, in charge at Namkham, just to say I was well, was in a Class A ward, and was being well treated by the Government. I gave the note to the Chief Jailer for censoring. If I had been an ordinary prisoner it would have been easy. The jailer would have read it, censored it, and mailed it right away. But I was no ordinary prisoner. I was a foreigner charged with high treason. The jailer had to send the letter to one department after another in the Government and it was very very late getting to Grace, who was worried sick about me. After that I wrote no more letters until I was released from jail, not even to my family in America. I was frightened lest some single word should be misconstrued as evidence of treason or some other crime.

To my astonishment, I seemed to hit the front pages in America. In no time I got my first cable from an old friend: "Keep your chin up. Let me know when you need my help." But my first airmail letter from America was not so helpful. Some professedly religious group in Pennsylvania or Ohio sent a lot of lugubrious tracts, ostensibly based on the Bible, with an anonymous covering letter. This group apparently does these things to any poor sucker who is thrown into jail anywhere in the world. The theme is: "Thank God you're in jail. Now you should realize at last what a pitiful sinner you are; so repent your ways lest God blast you and all yours."

God save us all! How *has* Christianity survived the ministrations of so many of its professors for so many centuries?

From the earliest days of my imprisonment until I was finally discharged, various others sent in similar comforting words and sundry religious publications. Some people were offended because I sent back the publications and refused to be bothered with them. The only person who did me good by sending me Bible texts was Emily's uncle. He really knew his Bible. The texts were invariably exactly what I needed. There was not the slightest sanctimoniousness.

Somehow it was offensive to me that everyone worried about my lack of faith—the faith that would immediately open the prison gates and send me back to Namkham. Now, although a medic, I flatter myself I know the rudiments of faith: the faith that can move mountains. I have even practiced it successfully, quite often. There have been thousands of times when, in the course of my surgery at Namkham and especially later when we were doing surgery all over the Shan State—on verandahs, in bazaar hovels, on the floors of grass shacks—when, as I say, I found myself in the midst of a worse surgical mess than anyone could have dreamed possible. On those occasions of torturing mental stress I would project my mind some millions of miles above the zenith and positively insist that God not let this poor soul suffer as a result of my being not as good a surgeon as I ought to be under the circumstances. And the results of those operations were usually all that could be desired.

After I was released from jail I began to get an idea of how many people of how many faiths had been pestering God to have me acquitted. There were Baptists, of course. But there was no particular reason, as far as I could see, why Roman Catholics, Anglicans, Presbyterians, Seventh Day Adventists, Buddhists and Jehovah's Witnesses should have thrown in their prayers in my behalf, let alone a few Hindus and Mohammedans!

Most touching of all was a letter I received a year later from a New Zealand woman. She was on her way to serve in China as a missionary when she read in a Hongkong newspaper that the Burma Surgeon had been thrown into jail. A few days later she was thrown into jail by Chinese Communists, and she suffered in a way no one ever suffers in a Burmese jail. Yet all the time she was in jail she prayed, not for her own release, but for mine! She attributed her own release after months in jail as a result of praying for mine. Now she is in Hongkong, waiting for the Communists to be pushed back so she can return to China and help her beloved Chinese. I can understand that woman. She is a kindred spirit.

My case was assigned to the Special Tribunal of the High Court, the very tribunal which had been first organized and presided over by U Kyaw Myint in 1947. Although it is theoretically a tribunal of the High Court, only the president of the Tribunal, Justice U Bo Gyi, was actually a High Court Justice. The thousands of political arrests had so littered up the calendar that there were not enough justices available of High Court status.

Treason is not a bailable offense in Burma, except for

illness. Since I *was* ill, U Kyaw Myint put up an application for bail, and I appeared, fortified by a certificate from the senior jail physician. This is where my Americanism did me damage. The only way I could keep my dysentery quiet long enough to appear before the court was to take a large dose of chlorodyne before leaving jail. I was determined there should be no accusation of contempt of court—the trials of the Communists were then proceeding with difficulty in the States—so on the appearance of the three justices I jumped to my feet at attention in my best Army style and, during the hearing, stood with my chin thrust to the skies.

This did me no good. Since my chin was not sunk on my breast the court decided the jail physician was wrong in certifying me ill. Furthermore, the court agreed with the prosecutor that I had far too much influence on the people of Burma. If I were not kept locked up I would be sure to suborn the witnesses. That gave me a laugh. The case against me had been in the making for a year while an *inspector* tried to suborn witnesses. My sister received a letter from one person whom the inspector had tried to suborn, which described the method used.

So I went back to jail, but I was only able to take fluid and slop, and I kept getting weaker. My condition was aggravated by a visit from a new and temporary prison official about whom I knew nothing. He asked me how I was doing and I said that thanks to the doctor's letting me take care of myself with my own medicines, I was beginning to get control of my dysentery at last. That tore it. The next day all my medicines were taken away.

A lot of my trouble must have been pure hysteria. It is my nature deliberately to forget unhappy things once they seem to be over. What the prosecution intended to accuse me of I could not know, but it surely must have been in connection with occurrences of a year before. I had records of those occurrences in my files in Namkham, but my friend the Inspector had taken pains to see that I had no opportunity to get hold of them. I could not possibly recall just which persons were present at every occurrence. I could not ask Shan girls to take the stand for me, because I was being tried on orders of their Commissioner. It would have been misunderstood. I was determined also to call no Karen to bear witness, though I finally had to give in and call Pansy Po, because only she and my sister, Grace, were witnesses to matters that dealt with hospital administration. And I could not call Grace, first, because she was an American and my sister, and second, because if she left she would certainly lose the hospital.

Finally I asked the embassy to send an American up to go through my files with Grace and Pansy and bring down the appropriate material. The embassy applied for permission, which was granted, and the material reached Rangoon as the trial began. Namkham was a military area, and the Burmese Foreign Department was worried about the safety of an American where there were insurgents. But by the time the emissary returned I was a nervous wreck, wondering if the important papers had disappeared.

Worried by my rapid loss of weight, U Kyaw Myint filed an appeal for bail directly to the High Court, which had the power to give bail at once. Then U Kyaw Myint was asked for a postponement of a few days, during which the Foreign Minister informed the embassy that if I would withdraw my appeal to the High Court, the Government would consent to my being moved to one of the small embassy-owned bungalows where I would be in a sort of private jail. U Kyaw Myint and I agreed this would be better than getting out on bail, for if I had been released we would never have heard the last of my suborning witnesses. The embassy turned an unlucky American out of his nice stucco bunga- low, made the property over to the Burma Government for the duration of my trial, and fixed up the air-conditioned bedroom for me.

After the chap in charge of my guard had made up his mind that I did not intend to try to escape or let anyone arrange an armed rescue, the rules relaxed. There was a nice rock by the side of the road (University Avenue), where I used to go out in the cool of the morning and again in the evening and sit. From there I watched free people riding in cars and buses and on bicycles and walking along without restrictions. This was a great sight. My favorites were an Anglo-Burman retired District Commissioner and his charm- ing Burmese-dressed teen-age daughter, who took their ex- ercise every evening on the far side of the road.

When I first sat on my rock in November, all my con- stables came out armed, with at least one inspector on duty too. Gradually the number decreased until finally they left their guns inside and just lolled around in sight of me. By the end of January frequently no one was in sight. But usually one or two or three would come just to chat with me; they had never insulted me by forcing their way into my room. Later they even allowed people who were passing by to stop and chat.

18

Trial

IT IS MY earnest conviction that everyone should be in jail at least once in his life and that the imprisonment should be on suspicion rather than proof; it should last at least four months; the case should, if possible, seem hopeless; and preferably the prisoner should be sick half the time. At least one false witness should be produced, or the prisoner will be robbed of the acme of experience. Only by such imprisonment can one really become educated. Only by such imprisonment can one discover who are really his friends and who his enemies. And only by such imprisonment does he learn what real freedom is worth.

A week after taking my case U Kyaw Myint informed me that three other lawyers wished to have the honor to assist in my defense. Honor! And to serve without fee! They were Mr. P. M. Beecheno, an Englishman; a Mr. Venkataram, an Indian; and a Mr. Chan, a Sino-Burman. A Burmese, an Englishman, an Indian, and a Sino-Burman, all defending an American for nothing. If Venkataram had to appear in another court, his place was taken by another Indian from the same office, Mr. Basu.

My imprisonment and trial took over five months. Some time was legitimately taken up in securing witnesses, most of whom had to be flown in from Myitkyina, Bhamo, Lashio,

Wide World

Dr. Seagrave watching the celebration in honor of his return to Namkham

Surgical block after bombing

Surgical block rebuilt

Pete Kalischer, Collier's

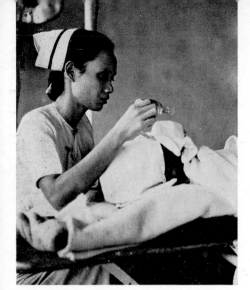

Nurse Esther Po administering anesthesi

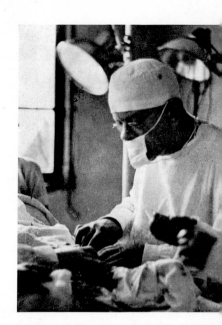

Dr. Seagrave operating

Two operations at once

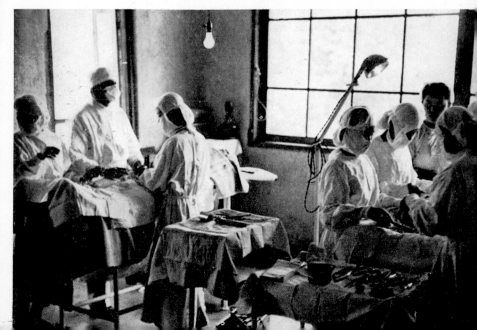

goiter operation:
Grandma Naomi,
Dr. Seagrave,
and Dr. Ai Lun

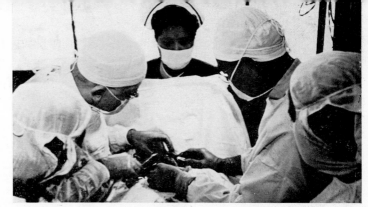

Ai Lun examining a patient   *USIS*

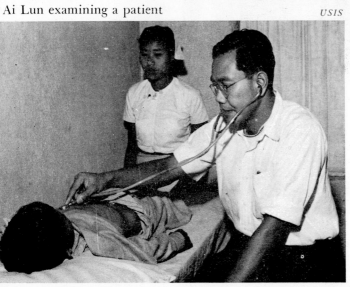

In the men's surgical ward   *USIS*

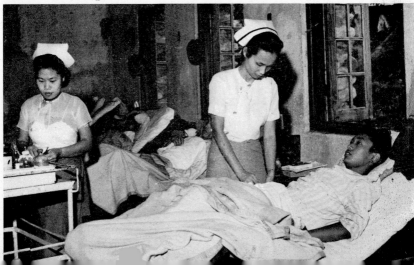

Pansy Po, center, and her two
Buddhist friends

Shan girls doing a flower dance

The first two Palaung girls
trained as nurse-midwives

Committee on Buddhist affairs

Dr. Seagrave, Dr. Ai Lun, and class after lecture

The Nurses' Home

Dr. Seagrave giving informal lecture

Dr. Grace R. Seagrave

Dr. Silgardo and Dr. Ba Saw

Old hospital, largely destroyed during war, now rebuilt

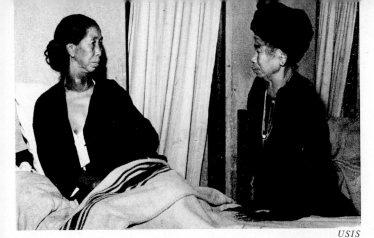

Patient receives a visitor from her jungle village

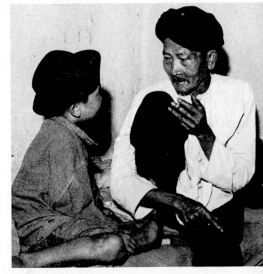

Father encourages a sick son

Nurse Emily shows a Chinese mother her first-born

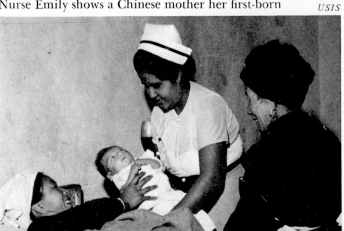

Dr. Seagrave, escorted to jail by armed policemen

Dr. Seagrave on release from prison

From hospital hilltop the Burma Surgeon looks down on the village of Namkham

Pete Kalischer, Collier's

Coolies pouring concrete for new building

Dr. Seagrave, Mme. Sao Shwe Thaike, Ambassador Sebald, and Sao Shwe Thaike, ex-President of the Union of Burma

Flags of the Union of Burma and of the United States on hospital grounds Namkham

and Taunggyi. Much more time was lost because there were at least three big trials going on before the Special Tribunal at the same time. This was extremely irritating to me, but I had no right to gripe. The other defendants were just as provoked as I was.

But most of the time was lost because court stenographers were not used. It seems that some stenographer had once been caught changing the evidence. When witnesses replied to questions, Justice U Bo Gyi synopsized what he thought were the important points and dictated a precis of the evidence to the typists—there was one typist with an English typewriter and one with a Burmese typewriter. It was most provoking. But I will hand it to Justice U Go Gyi. He made every effort to give the sense of the evidence in his précis without prejudice. When I was in the box, there were a couple of times when I did not feel that his précis of my remarks was quite correct, and he changed his wording to suit me. But—when a trial is very long-drawn-out and the record is not in the witness's own words, it makes it very difficult for even the most conscientious of judges to be completely just when he finally reviews all the evidence.

When the trial opened in November the first witness against me was Colonel Zow Gaung, who spoke in English. Mr. Beecheno conducted the cross-examination. Thereupon the Prosecutor had his witnesses—all but Colonel Hkun Nawng—give their evidence in Burmese, so that Mr. Beecheno could not even follow the evidence, let alone cross-examine. This made things much harder for U Kyaw Myint, but Beecheno consulted with him continually and took over the assignment of pulling my chin up and keeping it up. He came in regularly so we could abuse each other and call each other names—with a smile!

One of my best witnesses was Emily. I have never seen anything so extraordinary as the day she took the stand. I have learned a lot about the women of Burma in thirty-one years. The good ones are very shy around really big people, and these girls rightly looked upon the three justices as very great people indeed. Furthermore, Burman girls are terrified when they have to speak in front of a crowd. In all my class-room work and in conducting oral examinations they never really seem to pay attention to the questions, and you have to argue them into keeping to the point and not digressing. U Kyaw Myint saw the nurses only briefly before they went into the box. The Police Commissioner allowed me a whole afternoon with them, but I took only an hour to show them, in front of anyone who wanted to listen, the charges that had been brought against me so I could list for U Kyaw Myint the points with which they were acquainted. They received only one instruction from me: to tell the truth as they saw it, and tell it directly to the justices themselves, not to the prosecuting attorney or to the gallery.

Later Emily told me that before she was called her legs were trembling so she could hardly stand, but the minute she entered the box her fear suddenly left her. She bowed to the justices, took the oath, leaned on the rail, smiled at everyone in the room and looked to U Kyaw Myint for his first question. She listened intently, faced the judges and an-swered concisely, then turned for another question. When the Prosecutor stood up to cross-examine her she thrust her shoulders back a bit, raised her head and looked down her nose at him slightly as if to say, "See if you can catch me in a lie!" She listened as he asked her whether the facts were not this way and that way and t'other way. Emily smiled all over her face, turned to the justices and said, "No indeed, the facts were as follows." Her smiles wore the Prosecutor out. The difference between the appearance of the four defense nurses and the four prosecution nurses was extraordinary.

At the trial the Assistant Attorney General wanted to know if, when the insurgents came to Namkham, my De Soto was not in running order. I said that it was. Then I had to stand there and take it while he tried to convince the court that if Seagrave was not a traitor he would have climbed into that De Soto and driven to Maymyo or Lashio or Bhamo or Myitkyina to inform the Government that there were insurgents in Namkham. Now, the reader will recall that when the insurgents had first come to Namkham, practically all of our gasoline and a wheel from each of our motor vehicles save the De Soto and a jeep had been buried by my orders. The ridiculous thing is that I forgot all about this long before I was put on trial.

But the payoff came towards the end of my defense. U Kyaw Myint had called my driver as a witness to give evidence on some point. Then he turned him over for cross-examination. The questioning went something like this:

"How many vehicles did Dr. Seagrave have in running order when the insurgents came?"

"Three trucks, two weapons-carriers, one ambulance, three jeeps, one De Soto."

"Then Dr. Seagrave could have driven in any of those vehicles to Bhamo to inform the Government about the insurgents?"

"No, Sir, he could not."

"Why not?"

"When he heard that insurgents might come, Dr. Seagrave ordered us to bury all the gasoline and all the wheels of all vehicles except the De Soto and one jeep. He could not have gone anywhere."

The prosecuting attorney sat down hurriedly.

There was another interesting incident at the trial. My lawyers were deeply offended because I would not claim that I had given the medical stores to Naw Seng in fear for my life. If I had made that claim no one would have been able to prove me a liar, and I would have saved myself a sentence. But I was under oath. My personal safety had been farthest from my mind. Actually I was in a towering rage. All I had had time to consider was the integrity, first, of our precious and irreplaceable medical and surgical stores; second of our hospital and land, and third of our nurses' training school.

The prosecutor suggested that what I claimed I had done was appeasement. But by that time I was fed up, and I told him he could call it anything he wanted. I had given Naw Seng something I owned—a small fraction of what he demanded—and this had kept him from looting the hospital, from destroying it and the nurses' training school. When the nurses' training school was destroyed, it was not Naw Seng's action that did it; it was the Government's action, based on the false information it had received.

It was Sir Ba U, Chief Justice of the Supreme Court, who at last quieted the prosecuting attorney.

"During the Japanese Occupation," he said, "Japs used to come into my house and pick up things that caught their eye. All I could do was bow and smile and say, 'Help yourself, master.' "

I am a bit hard of hearing, especially when I am behind
a speaker and cannot watch his lips. And when the language
is English rather than American, and when, horror of hor-
rors, the Burmese is court Burmese rather than colloquial
Burmese, I am in real trouble. Throughout my trial it was
most irritating not to hear every word said. Sometimes I
was quite regretful that U Kyaw Myint's voice was not a
voice of thunder which would put the fear of God and the
nats (evil spirits) into witnesses who were reciting according
to instructions rather than telling the truth, the whole
truth, and nothing but the truth. But in Burma no well-
bred person is ever loud-mouthed, and his soft, well-bred
voice was far more effective than if he had shouted in modern
style. The witnesses and the justices could hear him well. It
really did not matter that my ears missed a lot. And those
innocuous, soft, sometimes slightly hoarse tones were so de-
ceptive that witnesses who were not telling the truth soon
had their necks stretched out so far that U Kyaw Myint
could easily lop them off with one blow.

On the day the judgment was handed down by the Special
Tribunal we went down to the courthouse an hour early, as
usual. The clerk of the court was a handsome young Burmese
who had looked askance at me all through the prosecution's
half of the trial. He viewed with alarm these white foreigners
who came into Burma and were guilty of subversive activities. During the defense he loosened up day after day, until
finally he spent a good deal of time smiling at me before their
lordships came in. On this morning their lordships were very
late. It is said that they were rewriting a few of the last
pages of the judgment. The clerk of the court was also late.
When he came in I knew I was a convict, because he most

assiduously looked everywhere but at me. He was most patently wretched.

Then in came their lordships. Now, Justice U Bo Gyi, the president of the Tribunal, was a most dignified gentleman. When their lordships were in their places he always smiled and nodded. Then everyone bowed and everyone sat. On this occasion Justice U Bo Gyi had no smile. He did not look at those present. If he had, I should have made an effort to smile encouragement. The Justice on his left began reading out the judgment. Justice U Bo Gyi himself acted for all the world as though he were a teacher of English who must be sure the pupil on his left made no mistakes. His eyes never for a moment left his own copy.

The judgment was that I was acquitted of the first charge. But I was convicted on the second and third charges. The sentence of the Special Tribunal was that I should be imprisoned for a term of six years' rigorous imprisonment. And so I went back to the Central Jail, this time as a convict.

I am told that U Bo Gyi had left his lunch untasted that noon, and that he did not sleep that night. For me the final irony in the judgment came when it said that I was like the man in the Burmese fable who, when he saw the Union of Burma gasping and about to drown in the deep waters of insurrection, reached out with a bamboo and pushed it under. What a powerful man I must be!

19

Pending the Appeal

ON MARCH 9th, on appeal to the High Court, the judges stated that they considered this a case where "the appellant should be treated very leniently"; they acquitted me of the second of the three charges and then reduced the sentence for the third charge to the term of imprisonment which I had already undergone. I was released from custody, and was free to do as I pleased as long as I did not leave the city of Rangoon. I was still a convict on that third charge—the gift of the instruments to Naw Seng—and could not return to Namkham. U Kyaw Myint now appealed to the Supreme Court to clear me of that charge and make me really a free man again.

Lawyers can be extremely uncommunicative when they so desire. Whether U Kyaw Myint knew that the hearing of my appeal by the Supreme Court would not take place for more than six months, I do not know. Perhaps he did, but feared that if I were informed of that fact I would have a hard time keeping my chin up. As a result, I went from week to week fully expecting that the date of the hearing would be set at any time. Had I known that it would be nine months before I could return to Namkham I would have sent for a team of nurses and set up a Rangoon branch of the Namkham hospital. Then I could have spent my time doing something constructive for the people. A wealthy Indian businessman actually offered free of rent a building in which to start this hospital. As time passed, however, one deterrent factor was that I knew that the loss of four or five of our best nurses would make matters much more difficult for sister Grace in Namkham.

It was then that I discovered how heavy the burden of a debt of gratitude can be. There was no possibility of my repaying my debt either to U Kyaw Myint and the other lawyers or to the embassy. It had hurt, therefore, to add to that debt by living in an American Embassy home. The home that my great-grandfather had built was practically empty, and sister Rachel would have been delighted to have me move out there. But at that time the whole compound was being used as a sort of concentration camp for Karens who had in one way or another been connected with the rebellion. U Kyaw Myint felt as I did that somebody would be sure to misunderstand if I went there to live. Mrs. Kyaw Myint owned a little property in the center of town two blocks from the American Embassy and the same distance from U Kyaw Myint's office. They both insisted that I move in there and live while awaiting the appeal. This would also be adding to my debt of gratitude to them, but when people are as charming as U Kyaw Myint and his wife and make you feel that you are doing them a favor when you accept a gift at their hands you cannot very well refuse. Mrs. Kyaw Myint's apartment therefore became my home after I was released from prison.

I felt quite awkward in front of my new neighbors. In the cool of the evening they all—Pakistanis, Indians, Chinese, Burmese—came out to sit on their front steps, and if I went

out to the movies, it was like running a gantlet. One Burmese lady about ten doors down helped to make me feel at
home. She recognized me in the faint night light of distant
street lamps and would tell all her visiting friends in an
undertone that that was Dr. Seagrave. This was the beginning of a new trend. Burmese had never called me Dr. Seagrave before. Only Anglo-Burmans and the English had
done that. Burmese would call me the American doctor or
the Namkham doctor, and if they were postwar patients
they imitated the nurses and called me Daddy, even though
they might be fifteen years older than I. Until my trial nobody knew my name or cared to know it.

The first few days after my release had been wonderful.
The freedom of riding around town in buses and taking in
a few American movies was a delightful experience after all
those months in jail. At many bus stops people of all nationalities who recognized me came up to shake hands
through the window and congratulated me on having been
released. I looked for enmity in the expressions of people
who recognized me and who might have believed from the
accounts of the trial that I was really guilty of treason
against their country, but no enmity was visible anywhere.

The day after I got out of jail I found that patients with
goiters had been waiting out my trial, refusing to be operated
on by anyone else. They obtained my address from U Kyaw
Myint and then from other patients, and I soon had a small
group of exophthalmic goiters which I was treating with
propylthiouracil until they could come to me later at Namkham. When one of the patients with a toxic adenoma
found out that my return would be delayed she went to New
York and had her goiter removed there.

But during those endless months in Rangoon while I waited from week to week hoping to get back to Namkham, the insurgents were not idle. They were continually blowing up the Rangoon water supply, and for days at a time the city had nothing but wells to carry on with. If Rangoon had ever recovered from the war it would have been quite bad enough, but sewers were still broken wide open. Thousands of people were living in little grass shacks on the sidewalks in the most crowded parts of town, and the cutting off of the water supply made things unbearable for everybody. The high-minded principles for which the Karens had originally claimed they were fighting had long since disappeared. Now there was no difference in action between their groups of bandits and the Communist groups, except perhaps that the Karens were slightly better organized. Without a constructive job life simply was not worth living in Rangoon.

But what I suffered during this period was but a small percentage of what Grace and the loyal Namkham staff went through. Everybody at Namkham had as much faith as I did in the Government of Burma. They expected me on every plane. Certain that I would be back at once Grace even accepted the first new group of probationer nurses to apply for training since the rebellion. There were twelve of them, of whom four were completely unfit to become nurses. When I did not return, this additional teaching became a very heavy burden for Grace to bear. When one lady on our staff heard I was not returning to Namkham, she went completely haywire, with the result that our best high-school teacher resigned, and life was made so miserable for four of the other completely loyal ones that they also would have left but for the love they felt for Grace. By the time the new school year opened in June she could not even be sure there would be a school, but pupils came from all over, and she managed to secure some poorly equipped teachers. However, she had to assume several classes in the school in addition to her teaching the nurses. This, coupled with the responsibility for the hospital, was more than her body could stand. During all that dark period Grandma Naomi was her mainstay in surgery. With Grace standing by to outline operative procedure, Naomi even did some emergency operations. The results of these, as I discovered a year later, were extremely good.

By July Grace's health was failing rapidly. Every plane from Lashio to Rangoon brought me a lengthy report about the hospital. It must have cost her a great deal to write these reports to me so regularly. They were always full of hope and showed her determination to succeed. By the end of July her health was so broken that she had to stop five times to rest and catch her breath during the hundred-yard walk from her house to the hospital. Although she covered up most of her symptoms, she had to admit that things were going wrong, and I received reports about her from the staff nurses also. The girls were so worried about her that they tried to insist on her using a jeep to ride to the hospital for rounds. But Grace refused: "If I ride round in the jeep somebody will report to the Government that I am not doing the hospital work properly, and they may take the hospital out of my hands before Gordon gets back."

On August 15, the anniversary of my arrest, she gave in and rode to the hospital for rounds. Afterwards she rode home again, lay down on her bed, and began her usual detailed account of the patients. When she reached the fourth page her handwriting began to go up hill and down dale, and she became unconscious in the middle of a sentence.

Two days later, at the exact time that I had been put into the Barr Street lock-up a year before, she died without regaining consciousness.

As long as Grace was conscious, Naomi, Esther, and Emily did not go over her head to obtain medical help for her against her will. But when she became unconscious the responsibility was too great for them to assume, and they sent word to Miss Elizabeth Taylor, a very charming American missionary in charge of the Kachin work sixty miles away at Nampaka. I later found that they had given her exactly the same treatment any doctor would have given after physical examination. Miss Taylor came immediately, sending a messenger on to report to Dr. Ai Lun at Lashio. By the time Ai Lun arrived Grace had already died. He and Miss Taylor took control and telegraphed me through the embassy that they were holding off the funeral as long as possible in hopes that I would come immediately.

When I got the news I am afraid I blew up. If a small fraction of what I said was reported to the Ambassador he would be quite justified in detesting my memory. However, I got action. An appeal was made by the embassy to the Government of Burma, and immediate permission was granted for compassionate leave. Thus I was able to return to Namkham to clear up Grace's and the hospital's affairs, provided I gave my word of honor to return to Rangoon immediately and to use commercial planes both ways instead of the embassy's own transportation. The embassy's plane could have taken me in four hours to Muse and I would have been in time for the funeral. Having to wait for the commercial plane to Lashio, I was too late.

It was long past dark when we reached Namkham, and the staff's reception was a quiet one rather than the exu-

berant shouting, laughing, and singing which would have
occurred if I had arrived before Grace's death. I checked
immediately on the records which had been kept by the
nurses from the time that she became unconscious, and I
had warm feelings toward the girls, who had made no
slightest error during a period of very great stress.

When Miss Taylor and Dr. Ai Lun had decided to carry
on the funeral in my absence, the word had soon leaked
down not only into the town but all through the valley.
Thousands came, by truck and on foot, to show respect to
the woman who had died serving them and keeping their
hospital open. People who were here say that the entire
hospital hill was black with people who could not crowd
into our little church for the service or into our little private
cemetery. I think Grace herself would have been astounded
at the tremendous respect and affection she had developed
in so short a time.

But everybody felt when I arrived that the funeral was
only half over and that the last half should take place
around the grave. By the time set the next morning, hundreds had come again to this second funeral. A Captain for
the Army; schoolmistress Ella, who had studied under Grace
in Rangoon thirty-five years before; Emily for the staff
nurses, Saw Tun Aung for the schoolboys, and Julia for the
pupil-nurses—each of them made addresses. I expected that
good speeches would be made by the first three, and they
were; but I was very touched when Julia spoke in glowing
terms and great clarity about how kind Grace had been to
her as a little schoolgirl in Loikaw years before the war. In
Burma people do not forget when you have done something
for them.

Almost all of Grace's files were connected with the hospital, and I took them over so as to straighten out the hos-

pital affairs while Rachel took care of the personal effects. While I was getting the papers together, I noticed that a large group of men representing the entire valley were gathering outside my door. The embassy had been fearful that suspicion would be again aroused against me if I permitted any demonstrations to be made in my favor at Namkham. The Government had taken my word of honor that I would return to Rangoon by the next plane. An inspector had been sent as a guard for a member of our embassy, and I took him out with me.

"Friends," I said in Burmese so the inspector would understand, "you know how much I want to return here, and I believe that you are just as anxious as I am for my return. Please do not compromise me by making any demonstration, and do not think that I am unhappy at your welcome when I ask you to disperse at once and go back to your homes."

Nobody said a thing except "How do you do"; then all shook my hand and left.

The rest of that day I spent on rounds in the hospital, outlining treatments for the nurses to follow. There was one more day for me to get acquainted with the new pupil-nurses and to talk things over with the older girls, who had just finished training under Grace, and with the staff. Ai Lun and E Hla, who had been at the funeral, had already gone back to their work in the hospital at Lashio.

As we traveled back to Lashio I thought a lot about the situation, and about Ai Lun and E Hla. There was still a matter of nobody knew how many months before I would be allowed back permanently. The appeal to the Supreme Court had not yet been heard. Grandma, Esther, and Emily are wonderful, but it is not fair to ask nurses to do a doctor's job in a hospital as important as Namkham. As we traveled

I wondered if Ai Lun would care to take a chance on loss of Government salary and his prospects for a pension, give up his position, and return to Namkham to take over as superintendent and thereby fulfill a plan I had had in my heart for years. I spoke to Mr. Sword at Kutkai and found that the American Baptist Mission would be delighted to assist me in securing his release from Government duty.

When we reached Lashio we put up at Ai Lun's house and I broached the matter to both him and E Hla, his wife. She was in my estimation a very superior nurse, who could guarantee either the complete success or the complete failure of my plans. On my part I undertook to repay for Ai Lun the debt which he still owed the Government for his training—roughly one thousand dollars. After they had talked the plan over privately they accepted the proposal enthusiastically. E Hla agreed to return to Namkham immediately to give strength to the nursing staff by her strong personality, with Ai Lun ready to follow when Government sanction should be obtained. Since I was personally prevented from obtaining access to Government offices, Mr. Sword agreed to carry out the negotiations for his release.

As we flew back to Rangoon the next day I felt considerably better. If eventually the Government permitted me to return and Grace knew that by her death she had brought about not only my return to Namkham but the return of Ai Lun and E Hla, I knew that she would have been perfectly satisfied to lose her life in order to gain these ends. As a matter of fact, I was a bit jealous of this sister of mine: She, like my father, had collapsed and died while she was actually serving the people of Burma. No one in Burma will ever doubt Grace's love for the country and its people.

In Rangoon, permission for Ai Lun's resignation from

Government service and return to Namkham as superintendent was given in as short a time as any government can reach a decision in a matter so important. About a month later it remained for the Shan State Government to make a very beautiful gesture: Although no financial grant had been made to help the hospital since the insurrection and although no grant had been requested, the Shan Government voluntarily made one in a letter which was really a citation of merit for Grace. This citation read "in recognition of the services rendered by this hospital to military and civilian personnel during the past year in an area not served by any Government hospital." I wondered whether this was not the first time that any government had voluntarily given a financial grant to a private institution.

The period following my return to Rangoon after Grace's death was even more difficult than before. The hearing before the Supreme Court was postponed again and again. It was a delight to be forgotten by the newspapers; newspapermen always worry me because one can never predict what they will write. But I could not do anything for myself. I had no way to enter the office of anyone of importance in the governments of either the Union of Burma or the Shan States.

By chance I did have one interesting contact. A tuberculosis sanitorium was to be opened by U Nu. I heard about this in the morning and wangled an invitation. A few minutes after my arrival it was announced that the Prime Minister had been delayed by an important conference, so everyone moved out to the side of the driveway and began chatting in little groups. When his car suddenly appeared, I found myself in the receiving line. U Nu descended at the head of the line. Then he came down, shaking the hand of each and saying "How do you do?" When he reached me I had my hand out and my very best smile spread all over my countenance. U Nu grasped my hand before he looked into my eyes. I could sense the shock he felt. Then his eyes sparkled, he gave me a warm smile and a handshake and said: "How do you do, Dr. Seagrave?"

At last the hearing before the Supreme Court took place. The judgment of the Supreme Court of the Union of Burma was: "The conviction and sentence on the third charge is set aside and the appellant is acquitted thereof." I was thus cleared of all charges against me under the High Treason Act. But my vindication by the court brought me no closer to Namkham. Various reasons were given to the embassy. One was that Chinese Nationalist troops had taken refuge in Burma and were only a few miles away from Namkham. It was known that my unit had served the Chinese National-ist armies under Stilwell. Therefore it was assumed that my sympathies were with the Nationalists. The second rea-son advanced was that I insisted on calling the Namkham Hospital the American Medical Center and actually had a signboard to this effect at our branch hospital at Kyukok where the Burma Road crosses into China. This signboard might prove offensive to Communist China.

So far as the Chinese Nationalists were concerned, the truth is this: The American officers who worked with the Nationalist Chinese Army under Stilwell soon became fed up to complete repletion. I served the Chinese longer and more closely than any other American. When they began to desert and to hide out with their arms and ammunition in Burma; when they began to tax the people in North Hsenwi State as if they intended to become Burma's government;

when they refused at the end of the war to return to China; when men whose wounds I had cured used our little private cemetery for a latrine—not a civilized Chinese custom—it was rather hard to look on even their sick in a professionally correct manner.

After Grace's funeral I had asked for an interview with the police, immigration, and other Union officials in Namkham. I told them that if they would authorize me to do so I would leave orders with the Namkham staff that no foreigner and no Shan or Kachin from villages in Communist China could be admitted to the hospital even in an emergency in the absence of a request by the Army, the Police, the Civil Administrators, or the Immigration Department. My purpose was to avoid even unintentionally giving asylum to a Chinese Nationalist, a Communist, or an insurgent. The officials were rather startled and asked me to modify my order to permit foreign patients to receive immediate treatment provided the staff notified the proper officials so they could screen the patients as they had time. To this I agreed. And later from Rangoon I strongly urged Dr. Ai Lun to see that this order was obeyed.

This policy has paid off many times. Nationalist spies and Communist spies have been caught in our wards and jailed. One day a Communist Chinese was caught in the act of stealing the Foreigner's Registration Certificate of a legitimate Burma-domiciled Chinese. No insurgent has ever been found trying to take refuge with us. When an undesirable character is dangerously ill, the Army or the Police, depending on the nature of the patient's offense, put a guard on him in the hospital until we can get him well. This is real co-operation.

As regards the offending signboard, I did not care what

people called this hospital, except that I did not want to call it "The Seagrave Hospital," as one Rangoon official suggested. All over Burma the Burmese just call us "The Namkham Hospital," and they come here because we treat our patients with the spirit of American doctors. I wrote Ai Lun from Rangoon asking him to see that the American Medical Center sign near our previous branch hospital at Kyukok be destroyed and that on letterheads he use the term, "The Namkham Hospital."

When Ai Lun took over as superintendent at Namkham it was natural that his eyes should see many flaws in our buildings and equipment and that he should want to spend money to correct all of them at once. With our limited financial resources one just could not do those things. I wrote him, therefore, asking him to hold regular staff meetings with our older nurses, who knew just what we could afford and what we could not afford, and I guaranteed to underwrite any expenditure to which they unanimously agreed. Ai Lun had never run a hospital before, but those girls, including his wife, had.

I listed also for Ai Lun what I considered the order of importance of various matters. To me the most important consideration is that we cure our patient without any excess expenditure of time or money. Second is the health, the welfare, and the happiness of the staff, since only with a really good staff can you cure patients. Third is the training of younger personnel so that they may replace older staff as needed. Fourth is essential repairs to building and equipment. Fifth is de luxe medicines to speed up cure. Last of all I place style and smartness.

In addition to the senior staff, which would constitute an

executive committee in all matters, professional and otherwise, I asked Ai Lun to interview important personalities of the area who were interested in our welfare because of our well-known policies, and to try to form a National Supervisory Committee. The plan was that such a body would meet with us regularly to supervise everything we did, and assume with Dr. Ai Lun the responsibility for correct governmental relations, and advise and help us with finances. Ai Lun did a superb job. He obtained the co-operation of fine men, men who appreciated the hospital more than ever as a result of my imprisonment; men from every walk of life from barber to prince of the blood; men of every Burman race as well as men of every race of domiciled foreigner—Chinese, Pakistanis, Indians; ex-officio officers of the Army and Police, ex-officio officials of the Union and State Governments. There are Mohammedans and Hindus; Animists; Buddhists; and Christians—Roman Catholic as well as Baptist.

Trying, from Rangoon, to help Ai Lun dig in as superintendent of the hospital was no easy job. It was much more difficult trying to give him a correspondence course in surgery, for in Lashio, in two and a half years, he had been permitted to do only a half-dozen operations as difficult as that for hydrocele. But all this gave me something to do and kept me from becoming too depressed.

20

Return to Namkham

BY THE middle of December my faith in the justice and fairness of the Burmese Government and its peoples was at an all-time low. Then one day a shadow fell on me from my open doorway and I looked up to see U Po Yone, a friend from Namkham. I almost kissed him. U Po Yone is a Shan who speaks better Burmese than Shan and is related to almost everyone I especially love in Namkham. His wife is a charming ex-schoolgirl of ours and a very lovely woman. He sat down and began to give me a long report on the hospital at Namkham and the first meeting of the National Supervisory Committee, of which he was a member. Then he went into elaborate detail as to how much they missed me at Namkham.

I interrupted: "See here, I have had about all I can take. I am at the breaking point. Do you boys, or do you not, really want me back at Namkham?"

"We certainly do want you back," he declared.

"How much do you want me? Do you want me enough to do some talking if I can arrange for a newspaper conference tomorrow morning?"

"You get them and I'll talk. I'll be here at eleven."

The only newspaper editor I knew was Ed Law Yone of the *Nation*. As soon as my visitor left I went to see him and told him about U Po Yone. Ed probably wanted a beat, for the next morning he came alone. U Po Yone had never talked to a newspaper editor before, and was trembling all over during the interview. Ed drew him out slowly until he got the story he wanted, and left. U Po Yone then contacted some Government officials himself.

The next morning the *Nation* splashed Law Yone's story on the front page. On the editorial page he had a column headed, "Send Seagrave Home." When they saw that, the embassy people had a convulsion, fearing I had started another international incident. But once they read the editorial through they changed their minds, for by "home," Law Yone, of course, had meant Namkham.

A few hours later the Home and Foreign Departments of the Union Government informed the American chargé d'affaires that there was no objection to Seagrave going home if he would give his word of honor to leave Namkham if ever ordered to do so by the Government. This proviso gave me to think, for when a Government orders you to do something, you do it whether you want to or not. The proviso indicated to me that there was a trace of suspicion still remaining in some minds that I had too much influence in north Burma.

I wonder if the picture of Burma and its government did not begin to emerge in its true colors at that moment? No autocratic country would care a thing about the public opinion of their own people. In keeping me forcefully in Rangoon, the Government had defied both American and British public opinion, as it had a perfect right to do both then and now. The younger a government, the more it must insist on its rights. But when they found Burman public opinion was on my side the matter was different. I doubt if any other country in the world would have been eager to permit a man once under suspicion to return to his job, even though their own Supreme Court had cleared him. It is a truly great country that will act contrary to personal suspicions because they honor their Supreme Court and because they value the opinion of their own public.

I lost several hours while the chargé d'affaires tried to get a written pass from the Home Department. No pass, the word came back, was necessary. Seagrave could go ahead and buy his ticket and refer any questions to the Government. Then the Union of Burma Airways sold me a ticket to Lashio as nonchalantly as if they had wondered for some months what was keeping me back. They told me no pass was necessary, but I was taking no chances. I would not go anywhere until I had informed every branch of the police of my intentions. So I went first to the Foreigner's Registration Bureau and changed my registered domicile from Rangoon back to Namkham. The final port of call was the most important—the headquarters of Special Branch II, which polices foreigners in Burma. Here, of all people, the officer in charge was my good friend Superintendent Lynsdale, who had arrested me in Namkham. There was a delay there because the Deputy Inspector General of Police could not believe Lynsdale's news until he had telephoned the Home Department. Then Lynsdale signed the paper which brought me back to Namkham. I still have that paper, with all the countersignatures that were put on en route to Namkham. One of them is that of the man who ordered my trial for treason. I would not lose that paper for anything. It is of interest to nobody but me, yet I keep it in the pages of my American passport, where it will not get lost.

There was time for me to perform my greatest duty of all. This was a last visit of respect and gratitude to U Kyaw Myint and as many of the rest of that great team of lawyers who had defended me as I could find. I am sure they had long before given up all hope of my being permitted to return. A year later they did not fail to remember me with a Christmas card, signed by all who were still in Rangoon.

It did not matter that I could not sleep that night.

The next morning it seemed only a few minutes after leaving the airport that we were circling the airfield at Lashio. Ai Lun had received my telegram, for there beside the field was my famed De Soto, with two drivers and a welcoming committee of Namkham nurses. There was also a jeep which had driven thirty miles from Hsenwi with one of our old staff nurses and her husband, a minister in the North Hsenwi State Government. The remainder of the crowd at the field were not there to meet me; they were there to see off some important officials. But they combined both tasks and gave me a rousing welcome, which made me want to weep more than my arrest had done.

While the De Soto and the Namkham contingent were collecting my baggage and buying gas, the Hsenwi nurse and her husband drove me in the jeep to all the necessary offices for countersignatures on my pass. All the officers dropped their other work and took care of my needs so efficiently that we actually reached the home of the Baptist pastor, where lunch was on the table, before the De Soto had collected my baggage.

My driver drove as far as Hsenwi, because I was not yet completely convinced that I was really free. There we were held up for an hour at a tea party, and two years later I was still being blamed for not having toured every side street and back alley in the town. But I was then still suffering from the effect of my trial; there was no way of knowing how much residual suspicion people might feel toward me.

But from Hsenwi I drove, and then I knew that at last I was really free. The gate opened automatically as soon as the keepers recognized me, just as it had before my troubles began. At Kutkai jaws dropped wide at the sight of me, and excited cries followed. But it was getting late, and I wanted a signature from the colonel commanding the battalion in charge of the Burma Road and Namkham Valley, so I drove straight through to Army Headquarters.

The sun was setting when we reached Nampaka. The mission is a half-mile from the main road and the De Soto was too low to negotiate the last quarter-mile of the side road. We stopped in the jungle while one of the drivers ran on to tell Miss Taylor I had returned. Not only she, but half the mission came out to greet me. Among them was an old Kachin pastor whom I had known from my first days in Namkham. He had not thought much of me before my arrest, even though I had once removed his gangrenous appendix. This time he grasped my hand, and the tears streamed from his eyes.

Long after dark we reached the beginning of the danger zone, the junction of the Burma and Ledo Roads. We stopped there to report to the Kachin army captain in charge, who turned out to be no less a man than the captain who had led the attack on the hospital in September, 1950. As soon as he recognized me he dropped everything, climbed into the De Soto and ordered a detachment of his men to follow in a jeep.

It was lucky for us that he did so. The Chinese Nationalists had been causing trouble, and the Army was really patrolling that road. As we reached patrol after patrol the captain leaned out the window and shouted:

"The Old Man's back. Let us through!"

His voice of authority carried us on without one stop.

At the top of the hospital hill I was given some surreptitious but extremely sweet kisses. Lucky it was dark!

Ai Lun and his wife were at the school Christmas party, which always comes a few days before Christmas so that the children can be home for the great day. My welcome there was much more subdued. The place was too bright with lights. Important officials were present, and I could report to them informally at once and wait a couple of days to report formally at their offices.

The next day I wanted to spend getting acquainted with patients and reacquainted with our staff. But instead, delegation after delegation kept dropping in to welcome me home. As I sat on the front steps of my house talking to the delegation of Christian villagers I noticed two Burmese standing to one side, taking notes. They were complete strangers, but as soon as the Christian Shans left, they introduced themselves as correspondents for one of the North Burma Burmese-language newspapers and handed me their press cards. They spoke no English, so I gave them their interview in Burmese, wondering if they would tear me apart. But they did not. When their interview appeared, it was written definitely for Burmese subscribers, who would want to know that the Old American Doctor was safely back at work in Namkham.

At Namkham the staff was worried. They did not want me to stay alone in my isolated house, nor did they want me to sleep with my doors unlocked. They objected when in the evenings I sat in my living room, which has eight-foot-wide French windows leading out to the screened front porch three feet above my little flower garden—a perfect shot for someone out in the dark. I promised to lock my doors, but I refused to sit in my bedroom at night or screen the French windows. If the people of Burma did not want me to live, there was no point in living. So I sat up late night after night, a perfect target, and I am still here. It was not until ten months later, when Chinese Nationalists were making themselves an unmitigated nuisance and Communist China was said to have brought down some big guns to their side of the plain, that my driver reported that the Army would appreciate it if I blacked out my windows at night. My front windows look out over the nearest part of China, and the Army's post is in line just beyond. I capitulated then, and blacked out my whole house.

I enjoyed that Christmas of 1951.

21

Patients

WHEN, after I went to jail, the number of patients had de-creased, Grace had closed up the Venereal Disease Hospital and the medical and maternity buildings, keeping all patients in the surgical block—the original Harper Memorial Hos-pital. On my return there were only thirty inpatients. The other buildings were closed, as much as buildings can be closed when you've never had money enough to replace bombed-out doors and windows. Thieves had stolen blankets, mattresses, and even beds, until on my return, the hospital owned a total of twenty-five decent blankets.

This constituted a challenge. In 1922 I had inherited a hospital with one inpatient and had built it up during twenty years of peace. But then I was just out of Johns Hopkins and wanted nothing but difficulties to surmount. In 1945 we had returned to a bombed-out hospital with no Burman patients but with a good staff, and had rebuilt it to a two-hundred-and-twenty-bed institution. And at that time I had the co-operation in no small measure of the United States Army, as well as prestige with the Burman peoples, and I had twenty-three years of invaluable experience to help me.

This time the hospital was still more or less intact, and we had a fair number of patients waiting for treatment. But now, in 1952, my body felt worn out by my experiences in Rangoon, and whether I had any prestige left among Burmans only time could tell. Perhaps my experiences during my trial, my loss of freedom and my ill health would prove one of those disguised blessings and make my services to the sick more valuable than ever. Certainly I could hope.

Ai Lun was busy on external affairs. He had conceived a health exhibit, the first in North Burma, and he was up to his ears carrying it out. Then he had our first baby show scheduled for the Independence celebrations early in January, 1952. As soon as these were over he was off with his health exhibit to Nampaka and Kutkai. I took over the sick. I loved taking over the sick.

A doctor does not advertise. His patients do the advertising. It was the middle of February before the sick really believed I was back in Namkham and would be ready if they came for treatment. Then we began to get those who had been sent away because Grace could not operate on them. One of the first was a nice Kachin woman with a pedunculated myoma which had delivered itself from the uterus. She had all of her pelvic organs matted together with disease. Less than fifteen per cent of her blood was still in her body—a person is not supposed to live with anemia as severe as that. After Grace sent her away she had gone to a surgeon who was not a gynecologist. He had explored the abdomen, taken one look into the pelvis, and had sewed the lady up again.

We got the hemorrhage under control and built up the patient's blood until her hemoglobin reached fifty per cent. Then we operated. She would never have withstood that three-hour operation if Grandma had not produced some old American Army plasma which she had hidden. As it was, the patient did not turn a hair, and her recovery was uneventful. In four weeks she had gone home to show people what could be done at Namkham. When she first came to me some friends of mine from her home town had written to our staff nurses begging them not to let me stake my reputation on this patient. When the operation proved a success these same fearful ones came themselves to be operated on.

There were three men who came in a series with very enlarged prostates. The first was an Indian. When he left for home, salaaming all over the floor, the two Burmese came, one a rich man, the other as poor as you can get and still eat once in a while. The rich man had had the right diagnosis made elsewhere, but the specialist had refused to operate. He had done only a cystostomy and sent the patient home. The poor man had severe hypertension in addition to all his other troubles. I couldn't bring his blood pressure down, and I rather hoped he would voluntarily go home to die. When he heard the rich man had pulled safely through his operation he insisted, and we removed his prostate, too.

That man is about fifteen years older than I, but he calls me Daddy as his daughters do, and he makes periodical trips to Namkham, a hundred and fifty miles by river, steamer and truck, to escort timid patients from his home town to us for treatment. Whenever I see him he hugs me and I him, and we thump each other on the back for five minutes, shouting and laughing, while the amazed nurses stand by and alternately giggle and wipe their eyes at the sight of this demonstration of second childhood.

Recently they had a World Health Organization day in a nearby city. My wealthy prostate patient was one of the distinguished speakers, and he declaimed about Namkham.

"At that hospital," an amused staff nurse of ours heard him say, "you are treated with astonishing kindness. I was a Burmese patient. Not one of their nurses is Burmese; they are Kachins and Shans. But you would never know it. There is no task which the patient needs to have done which is too dirty for them to do. You would think them incapable of feeling disgust."

Some of my Rangoon goiter patients came up for operation too. When the first one left, the whole family came to say goodbye as I stood in front of the nurses' home after morning chapel. To my horror my beautiful patient got down on her knees in the dirt to give me the threefold Burmese *shee-hko*. I tried to prevent her, but her father, a retired Government official, intervened.

"Leave her alone. This is our Burmese custom."

"I know it is, but I don't deserve it."

One day I had had too much of this shee-hkoing and asked Ai Lun what to do about it.

"By the shee-hko they wipe out any debt of gratitude which they may have been unable to pay with money, and they ask for a blessing," he explained.

After my months in jail, that explanation made sense. I wish I could wipe out my debts of gratitude to hundreds of people in Burma by some judicious shee-hkoing and at the same time earn a lot of wholehearted blessings! Now when a patient shee-hkos to me I put out my hand, pat them gently on the shoulder (in Burma you don't ever, but not *ever*, touch a person's head without good reason) and murmur a blessing. The patients then get to their feet, their faces shining with renewed self-respect, and, I believe, with some real affection for The Old Man who tried to help them.

Long before the rains our maternity block was flourishing as a separate unit, and the surgical block was full. The beginning of the rainy season had always been the end of our surgery—except for emergencies—because our valley is agricultural, and people cannot spare time away from their plowing and planting. During the rains we used to have only medical diseases—malaria and dysentery. On my return from Rangoon all this was changed. For the first two or three weeks of the rains we had a slump, but then surgery began to come in again by the jeep and truckload—people from the cities, merchants and traders, whose own work was decreased by the singlemindedness of the farmers. By the time the weather at Namkham had become so cold that the people from the Irrawaddi plain didn't dare venture out from their warmth, our own crops were in, and then Shan State villagers had begun to come in again.

Our biggest slump now is from the first of January to the fifteenth of February. Everyone goes home for the Independence festivities and for the really severe cold weather. Then they begin to pour in. Jeeps and trucks are chartered to bring whole groups from the same town or village. One day it will be patients from Myitkyina and points north. Again it will be a large group from Shwegu and Katha down the Irrawaddi. Another day it will be patients from Kutkai, Hsenwi, and Lashio. When Nampaka sends patients it is always in a group, preferably during one of the school's vacations. When one small village sends a contingent of patients it will, as often as not, turn out to be village-day, and there will be groups of three or four from many widely separated villages in the Kachin State and the Shan State, and even Kachins and Shans from Communist China, many of them with bullets stuck in them hither and yon.

There is a monthly illustrated magazine published in Burmese which has a question-and-answer section run by a doctor. In a recent copy a reader described her symptoms and asked what she should do. Apparently it was too much for the doctor, so he replied: "Write to Doctor Seagrave in Namkham and ask him about it." If my recent experiences had done nothing else they certainly had put Namkham onto the Burma map.

It is impossible not to glow when sick people regard your hospital as their last resort in time of trouble—a sort of Supreme Court whose decisions are final. But the sense of responsibility is overwhelming. What if we should fail people who trust us like that?

Since my return to Namkham a problem which we have always had has become a really serious burden, with no solution in sight. Namkham has no hotels or inns, and the Buddhist *zayats*—places where foot travelers may sleep without charge, cooking their own food and supplying their own bedding—are either always full of travelers or completely empty. Nobody wants to sleep in the open alone since the insurrections and the Chinese Nationalist aggression. There is no baby-sitters' union to sit and watch houses and children for weeks while parents come for operations. Thus, when patients come a hundred miles or more to Namkham for operations so serious that they cannot be done elsewhere they do not want to come alone, nor do they want to take a chance on dying alone in a strange place.

So every patient brings father, mother, brother, sister, and children along. Especially the children. And we have to put them up and put up with them. Except in the private rooms, only the patient gets a bed; the others are supposed to sleep on the floor. But it is not unusual to find the husband and one or more children sharing the mother's single bed. One man, as soon as the day nurses were out of sight, actually made his wife sleep on the floor while he took her bed. The night nurses had an emergency operation, making him get out and give the bed to his sick wife. One woman who had a pelvic tumor removed had brought a three-year-old child whom we placed in the maternity-pediatrics building. While the mother was in a critical condition the child kept escaping from the pediatrics ward and insisting that his mother lift him up on the bed and down again every ten minutes. Now that he has no mother, I wonder what he does.

If the children did not romp all over the hospital it would not be so hard to take, but they shout and scream until, when you are examining a patient, you can hardly tell a murmur from a rale. Twice we have had kleptomaniacs among these children. One took a hundred rupees and a gold locket and chain from a private room while the patient was undergoing an operation. The other had stranger tastes. He ran off with my operating glasses and hung them from a branch of our big red bougainvillea.

It has become the custom throughout Burma for the hospitals to expect relatives to bring in food from the outside for patients. We furnish food for patients, but when they bring their families along we do not furnish food for the families. The result is that the families cook for themselves and their sick members as well. This is a tremendous relief to us financially, but it raises new problems: We have to furnish cookhouses so they will not build fires in the wards.

When the cookhouse near the medical building is

jammed, even with families cooking in shifts, they start cooking in our laundry shed, much to the detriment of the hospital linen. A favorite cooking place for our private patients is on the verandah of the annex to our surgical building, just beyond our physical-examination rooms. It is really a sort of club they have there. If only my ears were not so deeply involved with rales and murmurs and if I had time to listen, I would undoubtedly pick up some of the world's most astonishing gossip in six languages.

It is easy to see that there is one criticism that cannot be leveled against this hospital: We are not unfriendly. We can truly claim to be a home away from home. Colonel Lapping, the last British Chief Medical Officer, called us "the happy hospital." We really are a family. I am Daddy; Naomi is Grandma; Emily is Auntie; Ngwe Nyunt is Mummy; Esther, Pansy, Silver Flower, Julia, and Dorothy are Big Sisters; the pupil nurses are Little Sisters. Only Silgardo is Doctor, and Ai Lun is Big Doctor.

The spirit of the nurses is wonderful. This must be one of the very few hospitals in the world where nurses and doctors sing or whistle on duty. I would not have it otherwise.

By December, 1952, the medical building had been reopened. By June, 1952, the Venereal Disease hospital was in use again as a contagious-disease hospital. Then we had to move the nurses and hospital diet kitchens to a new site beyond the nurses' home and use our former stone kitchen-diningroom building as an annex to take care of the overflow from the surgical block. There are so many surgical patients now that when they need pre-operative preparation they are admitted to the medical wards. On the day of the operation we transfer them to surgery and then, as soon as the critical period is over, they go back to the medical wards for final convalescence before the difficult trip home.

To my surprise, it has been harder to wipe out doubts in America than in Burma. I had been back in Namkham only a few months when I received a letter from a man in Ann Arbor. He had learned through a friend in the State Department that I had been allowed to return to Namkham. Was I being permitted to do my work or had the Government taken away my hospital? When I replied that not only had the Government *not* taken away the hospital but that Union Government, State Government, and Army were co-operating in a way I had never experienced before I was arrested, he sent us a gift of thousands of dollars which helped put us back on our feet, bought linen and blankets, urgently needed surgical instruments, and other equipment. A second gift was on condition that I prove to him the Government's approval of our work by obtaining import licenses for American drugs and laboratory equipment.

To obtain these licenses Dr. Ai Lun and Committee Member U Po Yone went to Lashio, Taunggyi, and Rangoon. At Rangoon Ai Lun was advised by Government friends to hold a press conference to clear up any misunderstandings which might exist with regard to the management of this hospital and its contribution to the welfare of the country. Ai Lun did such a splendid job that the Prime Minister is reported to have telephoned the Minister of Health immediately to find out ways and means whereby the Union Government might assist this institution. Certainly the import licenses were issued without delay, and the drugs and laboratory equipment and five hundred ex-Pullman Company blankets are here.

I believe Ai Lun grew up at that moment. Previously he had had a great deal of trouble with his surgery. Since then his surgery has improved so rapidly that he has taken over all our gastric surgery and a great deal of our gynecology as well.

By the end of 1953 we had so many private patients that every semiprivate nook and cranny in the place was filled with patients who supported our charity work, and ninety per cent of our cases are charity cases. People were even reserving rooms in advance and urging patients already occupying private rooms to get out so they could take over and have their surgery done. The Hospital Committee therefore ordered me to draw up plans at once for a two-story building to furnish eight large, eight medium, and eight small private rooms. They were to be responsible for the cost. I love to be ordered around *that* way. This is the first time anything had ever been started in Namkham except as the result of misery and long planning on my part, and the use of all the ingenuity I possessed.

22

Burma Nurses

For myself I was so grateful to be able to return to my work that although no restrictions were placed on my movements I put myself under what amounted to a hospital arrest. Unless I was almost forced to do so I never set foot outside of our hospital property, not even to go to the town of Namkham, never even for a drive in the car.

Of course I missed a lot of fun by this self-arrest. A born traveler, I love every part of Burma so much that I do not dare let my imagination run riot. There was a deep longing to revisit every one of those lovely spots where we did surgery all over the Shan and Kachin States before the insurrections. I wanted to meet all my old friends again and chat with them and see how many children they have. I would love to do surgery again in all the states for the hundreds who cannot obtain surgical attention.

But I have the best of all. I have this hospital. And since I do not go elsewhere, people come to me. When three Inthas with complications drove five hundred miles in a jeep from Inle Lake for surgery and healed up with perfect results in spite of the complications it was all I could do to keep from kissing their scars goodbye. When a Buddhist monk who was partially paralyzed came here all the way from Homalin, where we crossed the Chindwin with General

Stilwell in 1942, and was so grateful for his moderate improvement, I almost wept. If I do suddenly get a longing for other places and other friends I take one look at this valley, and I am perfectly happy again.

Only three times in two and a half years have I been more than a couple of miles from this hospital. The first time was to perform an emergency operation on a Kachin patient sixty miles away—an operation which, at that time, Dr. Ai Lun could not perform. I asked him to get written permits for me from the civil and military authorities and suggested that the company commander send a soldier along to see that I did my duty and nothing but my duty. When I stopped my De Soto at the post not one but two soldiers climbed in.

"Gosh!" I thought, "are they so suspicious of me that they don't dare trust me to only one soldier?"

"The doctor doesn't need to be afraid," said the corporal, as if in answer to my thoughts. "We will protect you from all danger."

I was speechless. I had wanted the Army to furnish a soldier to spy on me. Fear of personal injury never enters my mind in Burma. But the Army had sent a corporal and a private to see that The Old Man was not hurt.

In Burma the private-enterprise hospitals are all like mine at Namkham. Doctors are given what is considered a living wage. They are considered to be full-time men. Any fees given by patients, whether for hospital service, operative work, or for calls paid in the town and countryside, are most definitely the property of the hospital. I have followed this rule myself even to the extent of being occasionally hostile when patients tried to give me gifts in kind because they knew I would accept no money for myself. Since long before

World War II, I have refused to take in my hand money given by patients, but have made them pass it over to the nearest staff nurse, or even to a pupil-nurse, if I knew what that pupil-nurse was made of. Then the money went straight into the hospital's contribution box, from which the staff nurse turned it over at regular intervals to whoever was acting as hospital treasurer. This was no insult to the donor, for it followed the tradition of the old days when a ranking Buddhist priest did not take in his hands the contributions in money given by donors. The money was accepted by a novice and the priest murmured a benediction.

This always makes a great impression on patients. All the races of Burma are by nature generous in making contributions to worthy causes. They are not nearly so anxious to be forced to pay exorbitantly for services rendered by someone already on a salary. Twenty years ago I discovered that hospital receipts were much greater if I left the presentation of bills to the chief nurse. Few patients could fool her about their private financial condition. She could explain how the hospital was financed, and they would believe her explanation. The only people who are actually billed by us since the war are Europeans who demand a bill— and even then we seldom comply—and any person who demands a private room or unnecessary treatment. For the rest it is our custom to point out to patients, from an itemized list if necessary, how much it has cost us to treat them, how much the operation was worth, and appeal to their generosity to assist us in our tremendous task of serving the poor who cannot pay at all. In a large proportion of cases the patient, if he can possibly afford it, pays us more than we would have demanded.

But this system is very hard on a doctor who is really

worth a lot and who is on a standard Government salary. I am convinced that the correct thing to do is to pay the doctor according to his worth, whether in a Government hospital or a private-enterprise institution, and then throw him into jail for accepting bribes if he lets his work slip and spends his time in private practice for his own benefit. After all, what difference is there in such a doctor and a salaried politician or police officer or customs official who even *accepts* a bribe, let alone *demands* one, as the salaried doctors do? Yet Burma accepts this custom because the English permitted it. Now there is evidence that the Burma Medical Association will do something to cure this situation.

Before the war in Namkham Dr. Ba Saw and Dr. Tu set the example by serving for less than they would get in a Government institution, because they were being paid a bare living wage supplemented by a very great deal of training in surgery. After the war, because they had become experts, they received more than doctors of equal rank elsewhere. Now we pay student doctors Government rates plus training in surgery. A very few object, and since they are inferiors, the sooner they leave the better.

With us, nurses are on the same basis as doctors. Before the war, aside from one or two like Naomi, who needed the larger salary to put younger brothers and sisters through school, the very best of our graduates remained with us on half the salary which they would have received from the Government just because, with us, they would continue to learn and would have a far greater amount of really difficult work to do, especially in surgery and obstetrics. Gifts that they received in kind were shared with all the nurses, or sold and the money used for a picnic or entertainment. Money

gifts made to them by grateful patients were hospital property and were used for the regular work of the hospital. No
staff nurse ever objected to this. Pupil-nurses who tried to put
the squeeze on patients, refusing to give them the care they
needed unless their palms were greased in advance, did not
remain in training after such actions became known.

Often on my lecture tours in the United States I have
been asked why I have accentuated the training of nurses
rather than that of doctors. The answer is simple: Doctors
were not available. In 1948 there were two hundred less
available in Burma than the English thought sufficient in
1940. Far too great a number of the prewar doctors were
Indians. Indians can be very good doctors indeed, and Burma
will find it hard to repay her debt to the great Indian doctors
who have served all over the country—the doctors who
learned at least the Burmese language, and some Kachin
or Shan as well, if they were assigned to those areas. But
for the Burmese a foreign doctor is no substitute for a good
Burmese doctor.

When I first reached Namkham in 1922, we had a
twenty-bed hospital, and the largest number of inpatients
treated in any previous year had been twenty-eight; that is,
about one or two beds filled per day. For equipment we had
a lot of wastebasket instruments and a pressure cooker. There
was a Karen doctor on the staff, more than sixty years old,
with no knowledge of surgery at all and quite beyond the
stage where he could be taught, let alone the fact that he
was convinced I was insane when I told him I was going to
do major surgery. As an assistant he was out of the question.
It was fifteen years before I could find a superior young
doctor who was eager, willing, and able to study surgery
with me.

The only possible solution was to train my own nurses. The Frontier States had no graduate nurses from their own states trained in Rangoon, Moulmein, or Mandalay. I imported two plains girls from Moulmein, but each ran away within a year. Girls from the Burmese plain are just not willing to work in a place like Namkham, a village on the border. Even the capital cities of Lashio and Taunggyi with their social life, possibilities for private practice, and Government-service prestige were unable to import enough nurses from Burma either before or after the war. Girls of the Burma plains wanted to stay in their own plains, as they had every right to do.

The location of our hospital in Namkham is an excellent one, for good reasons. The first of these reasons is, and should be, health. Namkham is at an altitude of two thousand five hundred feet, which makes it cool the year around (we have about fifteen very sticky days a year and no sticky nights) but which also makes it one of the most malarious valleys in Burma; and the dysentery here can be very bad indeed. Our diseases are absolutely typical of all the Frontier States and not typical of Burma Proper.

When I was Chief Medical Officer of the Shan State and North Karenni State in 1945–1946, I wanted to open a hospital at Bawlake in Karenni, but was told it was too unhealthy a place. What is a hospital *for* but to be in an unhealthy place? Sanitaria, yes: Put them in the health resorts, by all means; transport your patients there. They are going to be there some time and will be able to use a good climate. But keep your hospitals where the sick, the urgently sick, are. And if you are going to train nurses for the Frontier States, where do you want to train them? Where they will be nursing patients with the diseases they will see or the diseases they will not see thereafter in their own home areas? A look at the map will show that Namkham is about as centralized for the Frontier States as any other heavily populated section.

The second of these reasons is that Namkham is not a great city. Nurses' training schools should be in great cities where the nurses will have every facility for enjoying themselves in their spare time? Perhaps. But incidentally, the nurses will become so sophisticated and citified that they will never go back to their home areas to work and, if forced to do so, will break their hearts, right in their old home town.

People have said to me: "Doc, you have no right to keep such perfectly charming girls in such an out-of-the-way place. They have no chance to meet the right kind of men, men of their own caliber." That is agreed. I have fretted all my life because the total number of real eligibles was so limited. Now, with the extraordinary changes which the Government of Burma has made in the type of men whom they are sending to the Namkham valley as civilian officials and Army officers, our problem is beginning to take care of itself.

But since Namkham is not a city, our graduates are the only ones that will go back and serve in primitive areas and enjoy it. They haven't become so sophisticated that they aren't fit to live.

During my first term of service we trained six nurses. In my second term we built the stone Harper Memorial Hospital, which is now our surgical block, and trained a lot more nurses, several of whom understood English, the first of this latter group being Dr. Ai Lun's wife, E Hla. And we started to employ doctors in hopes that we could make surgeons out of some of them. We adopted a Shan boy named Ai Lun and helped put him through high school preparatory to college and a medical degree with the conscious purpose of having him ready to take over from me when I died.

In Namkham the nurses take histories rather than doctors. Now, why do our nurses learn to take histories? Necessity again. During those first years when I took all histories myself, I almost always had to use a nurse for an interpreter. So why should both of us waste time at it? Let the nurse take the best history she can while the doctor is busy with someone else. It does her good. It teaches her to watch for symptoms and signs. Not interpret them, no; the doctor interprets them. It does the patient good, too, especially in a country like Burma, where the patients from the jungles and most of those from the cities are not quite sure they ought to have come to the hospital in the first place. Telling a nurse all about it gives the patient back his confidence. Then the doctor and the nurse get the patient into an examining room and the doctor looks over the nurse's history, which may be a pretty woeful effort but which gives the doctor the hint as to what further questions should be asked. He fills in the nurse's history and has saved about half an hour of his fairly precious time.

Our primary adaptation, then, has been to fit the nurse to do everything she could to extend the doctor's usefulness. To that end I never did a thing I could teach a nurse to do well. Being women, and women with brains, they soon learned to do many things better than I could myself, and they still can. I often ask advice from our top nurse, Grandma Naomi, and she is never wrong. I now take advice not only from our senior staff nurses but from our junior staff as well.

And I do not have to apologize for the kind of girls we

turn out. If the fame they won in the United States Army during the war is not sufficient, we can produce a bit more evidence. Six of our nurses have been sent to the States since the war. The U. S. State Department sent Koi and Sein Bwint to the Mayo Clinic for a year and a half. If the nurses' magazines in the United States were not prevaricating, those girls did extremely well, working side by side with some of the best nurses in the world. I sent over four girls out of the money I made from my lecture tours. Esther and Pansy Po went to Louisville for training as laboratory technicians in the School of the State Board of Health rather than straight postgraduate nurses' training. But they were competing with American boys and girls who were graduates of colleges, and I have letters from the doctors who trained them, stating that in spite of their having to study in a foreign language, they held their own. Hla Sein and Ruby have had five years in the Margaret Hague Hospital in Jersey City. Now the Philadelphia General Hospital has accepted Ruby.

Our second adaptation of our nurses' training was also forced on us. By the end of my first term of service, western medicine had become very popular in the Kachin substate of North Hsenwi. Also the big Shan-Kachin valley of Mong Paw, about forty miles away in the mountains from Namkham, demanded some medical attention. My first graduate was from Mong Paw, and the people there wanted her to return and open a nursing-hospital where she could take care of ordinary emergencies and ordinary diseases and maternity cases and forward all the really sick people to us.

That first venture was a profound success. Transportation forty miles to Namkham by stretcher had been a difficult undertaking. The sick did not like to go through it when they were not sure I would be able to do anything for them after they reached Namkham. With a nurse there to assure them that they needed me and that I could help them, they came. And then other valleys demanded similar nursing hospitals, and by 1941, Englishmen who knew said that North Hsenwi State had the best medical attention of any area of similar size in Burma.

It was not until my third term that I was able to learn whether or not I could really teach a doctor surgery. Then I trained Dr. Ba Saw, whom I sent to Louisville General Hospital for a year of training and who, on his return, is supposed to have been the cause of all my troubles with the Burma Treason Law. Dr. Ba Saw was such a success that before the war we tried to get accredited as a hospital for internes. But my race and religion were wrong. The English did not want Burmese internes trained by an American. Next we started training Dr. Tu; and then, during the war, Dr. San Yee, the Number Two ranking Shan doctor, joined us in India, and we taught him as we fought.

The whole Shan State and more than half the sawbwas think a lot of the girls who have graduated from Namkham. No one was more delighted with them than Sao Shwe Thaike, sawbwa of Yawngwhe State, who became the first president of Burma. He had sent girls to us for training for years before the war. Once when I apologized to him because some of his graduates had married without serving as much as a year in his hospital he answered:

"Doctor, I don't care if they never serve a day in the hospital after graduation. I know that after they are married they may never even try to make money in private nursing. But I also know that no matter whom they marry or where they settle their home will be a small dispensary and public-health center."

As he had said formerly, we had a "Union of Burma" fifteen years before the Union of Burma was created as a political entity. Now Namkham is a Kachin-Shan area. It is not a Karen area. There isn't a Karen village within three hundred miles of us, and the nearest Karen Quarter in a town is at Bhamo, seventy-two miles away. In Namkham the Karens live scattered among the Shans and Kachins, and they love it. The Karen girls who come here for training come from all over Burma, but have never constituted more than a quarter of the enrollment of our training school. At present there is one Karen and one half-Karen in training with fifty-nine Shans and Kachins and Palaungs.

Recently the Government of Burma has promoted a conscious effort on the part of the people of each race to wipe out the old interracial hatreds. It is a common thing now at banquets for the guests to be members of several races and for each race to toast the good qualities of the others. I have been fighting for this kind of comity for thirty years. And fifteen years ago we had obtained it in our hospital and in the nurses' training school. Now that this fight is being carried on by the Government and by the people themselves, it is safe, I think, to leave it in their hands. Nowadays you actually hear Burmese, Kachins, Shans, Indians, and Pakistanis praising Karens. Kachins, Burmese, and Shans have started marrying our Karen nurses. The next step will be a melting pot.

At the cost of her life Grace had kept the nurses' training school and the high school open as well as the hospital. In the spring of 1951 as soon as she heard I had been released, she had accepted a new class of nurses. From this class six girls are with us now, doing the last of their four years of training. All are worthy of being kept on as staff nurses. If one is lacking in one variety of work she excels in another. When they had finished one year's training it was necessary to put them in charge of wards under a staff supervisor. Now, during their fourth year of training, one after another alternates as supervisor of the medical building. They are really junior staff nurses, and as this year goes on we will be able to specialize them according to their especial talents. Two are Shans. One is half Shan, half Karen. The other three are Kachins.

Before I was arrested we had as a staff nurse a girl whom I brought into this world when she was born. In our present senior class is a girl who was born because I operated on her mother for sterility. She was followed by a sister and four brothers. The relationship between that family and myself is so close that at times it becomes funny. If there is some world-shaking decision to be made with regard to any of the six children, the father considers it his duty to come down from his village at the top of a mountain in Momeik State and ask my advice. If one of them, while in school here, needs a parental decision he or she comes to me, and unless I insist that the parents be called in, my decision is final.

In each of our recent classes is some girl who brings back memories. There are several whom I brought into the world. One is an orphan whom we saved alive in our pediatrics clinic and then had adopted by a superior family that had no children of their own. And this year we accepted for training the daughter of a nurse who graduated here more than twenty years ago, the first second-generation Namkham nurse. I am beginning to feel old.

There is now only one full-blooded Karen nurse in training. Her father was a miserably paid missionary to the Kachins long before she was born. She is trilingual. When she speaks Burmese it is exquisite Burmese. Her Kachin is exquisite Kachin, and you have to look at the shape of her head to realize it is a Karen speaking and not a Kachin. She speaks her native Karen only when other Karens insist on it. In her second-year class she is one of two who can understand my English lectures, but she takes fluent Burmese notes on my Burmese lectures so that she will have the subject in two languages and be sure to understand. Very appropriately, her parents named her "Miss Delicate."

When I was released I was astonished to learn that wealthy Burmese families were still employing Karen girls to take care of their children, in spite of the rebellion. I asked a Burmese friend who had been vigorously condemning Karens about this.

"It's the men we Burmese despise," he declared. "If the men were like their women we would have no quarrel with them. No one denies the exquisite gentleness of Karen women."

Our present group is about a year behind Rangoon styles, for they don't receive enough money to be able to keep up with new fashions. But something new has been added since I came back from Rangoon, something which, to me, is absolutely fascinating. This is the posed expression which a girl selects after many months of close study of her best features. We did not have this before Independence. I wish I could let you really see what I see.

There is a Shan girl here from a nearby backwoods town. Her mother has not the slightest taste in clothes, and when

"Golden Victory" came here she wore jackets and *longyis* whose colors clashed and bodices far too tight for her. At Namkham she immediately sensed the difference between herself and her city-bred classmates. And she was ashamed, for as soon as her father could spare her some money she purchased tasteful clothes. But in other ways she had prepared herself well. Her naturally beautiful lips are set in an expression of complete serenity, and unkind remarks which I have heard made to her never disturb that serenity. Albeit she holds her chin up and looks down her nose at people whom *she* considers arrogant, there is not a microscopic trace of arrogance in her spirit. On this point hundreds of patients will agree. She keeps her chin up to show she can take it if necessary. And I believe that she looks down her nose at you because if she really lifts her rather heavy eyelids to look up at you, she knows that she will develop wrinkles in that serene forehead of hers and look worried. I have known her to be worried often, but no stranger would see a sign of worry.

Then there are two Kachin girls who have chosen to keep their lips pursed up slightly, looking for all the world as though they were waiting to be kissed. But they are not waiting to be kissed, as you can see if you pause long enough to look at those arched, arrogant eyebrows. This too, is a pose. They selected these expressions after careful study as the best protective device against being hurt. And though they have been hurt, they never *look* hurt.

One of the most charming is the little Kachin girl whose natural grin shows the gums above her upper teeth. The more hurt she is—as when she simply cannot remember the answers to my questions in class—the more she smiles that beautiful natural smile, and the more do her dark eyes sparkle. It really is a catastrophe for me to have to give her a zero, but she never fails to bestow a last smile and sparkle on me when she has seen my fingers unwillingly trace out that zero. This girl has her smile and her sparkle in spite of, or perhaps because of, an osteomyelitis in her forearm. She had suffered from this for years before coming here. As she came out of the anesthetic after I operated on her she began smiling, and she smiled through every painful dressing. It will take a lot to break the spirit of a girl like that.

One Kachin girl has adopted still another protective device. She keeps her lower lip advanced just a trifle beyond her upper lip as if to say, "Hmpf! You! Just try to hurt me if you can!" But this device just does not work. Her feelings get hurt, and she bursts out crying when nobody has done a thing wrong, and she has been capable of becoming unreasonably and overwhelmingly angry at other nurses without just cause. This is too bad, for when in her right mind she is an exquisitely sweet girl and has one of the seven best brains I have ever trained.

Three girls think they are attractive when they pout, and have pouted so continuously that undoubtedly they pout all night long while they are asleep. But I would rather have them pout as a defense measure than adopt the ferocious scowl which one of their classmates—a girl who is a terrific clown in the absence of any member of the staff—adopts when she comes to us to make reports. This scowl is also undoubtedly a protective device, but it is very hard to take.

We have one full-time pre-nurse now. She is the only girl with European blood we have ever had. She is half Scots and half Lushai from the Lushai Hills in Assam. She is also the only girl we have ever had with a full-blown English name, middle initial and all! Silver Flower picked her up on her vacation in Lashio. Her previous life had been most unhappy. Also she had a goiter, terrible tonsils, and a bad appendix. After all her surgical troubles had been attended to she stayed on, one of the cleanest, sweetest sixteen-year-olds I have ever met. Her Lushai Hills education does not count in Burma, but she is learning Burmese so rapidly that it is a continual astonishment to me. Already her Saturdays and Sundays in the wards are proving a blessing to our patients.

At many of our gatherings the nurses sit on the floor, and the grace with which Burman girls do this is fascinating. Bending over, they kneel, and then suddenly they are sitting on the side of the pelvis with their feet tucked under them to one side. When the cramps become sharp there is a graceful twist, and they are sitting on the other side of the pelvis. They are far more graceful than the much-lauded Japanese. If I sat like a Burmese girl for fifteen minutes, I would not be able to walk for a week.

Each new class has arrived just in time to save the hospital from being swamped with work. By the time the older girls are beginning to show signs of complete exhaustion, new girls arrive. The arrival of a new class, of course, increases the burden of teaching. But in this hospital, the doctors and Grandma, Emily, Esther, and Pansy teach the junior staff. The junior staff teaches the senior pupil-nurses. The seniors teach the juniors, they the sophomores. And so on down.

We still have disciplinary problems, even on our present basis. Dr. Ai Lun can use force, but he does not like to. I cannot. There is one thing, however, I can do, and it is much better than force. I can appeal to patriotism, and patriotism really exists in Burma now.

23

Friends

THERE IS one story that ought to be told. But it is not about a nurse; it is about a man who is as essential to this hospital as any doctor or nurse on the staff. His name is Ai Sai—Number One Big Brother. When I first saw him twenty-eight years ago he was about ten years old. He was a forlorn, dirty little orphan Shan boy who had existed on handouts from the good-hearted people of Selan, twelve miles away. But in his bladder he had a huge urinary stone as large as two walnuts fastened side to side. This had caused him to suffer exquisite torment since he was old enough to remember.

When my surgical reputation reached Selan, Ai Sai decided to come to me and have his stone out. There was no transportation in those days, and he had no one to carry him. He walked part of the way until his strength gave out. Then he crawled on all fours until he dropped down on the hospital verandah. Since we had no proper operating room then, very poor light, and only wastebasket instruments, the operation was not easy. I was not pleased with the job, but Ai Sai's pain was stopped.

After his wounds healed Ai Sai refused to leave. He had no money to pay me and could not bear the thought of leaving without repaying me somehow for stopping his pain. Would I not please let him work for the hospital without wage until he felt he had repaid me? There was nothing really useful this boy could do for the hospital—so I thought. But if it would help him retain his self-respect I could at least give him nominal work. I let him rake leaves, and he ate in the hospital kitchen.

He soon found his own job. He scrubbed the kitchens and the nurses' dining rooms. He pared potatoes and pre-pared other vegetables to help the cooks. He went with them to the bazaar and carried up their heavy baskets of food on a bamboo yoke over his shoulder. While various nurses were eating their meals he overheard them griping about having to wash the blood out of operating-room linen. Then that became his next job. He took all our dirty linen—hospital linen can be extremely dirty—down to the little rill that flows south of our land and washed it by laying it on a huge rock and pounding the soap into it and the dirt out of it with a flat club.

By the time the new school year opened, I had fallen in love with him. I suggested that he let me put him into the school, for he had a high I.Q. He refused. He already felt himself an essential part of our hospital work and felt, I am convinced, that he had a share in every patient's cure. He did not want to lose his sense of self-respect by accepting more favors from me by going to school.

Then I rebelled. He had more than repaid his debt of gratitude to the hospital. I made him accept a salary, the immense sum of three dollars a month. About that time, we put up our first big stone hospital and installed running water and flush toilets. Our patients were and still are naive. They thought anything would flush out of those toilets—

sticks, stones, bandages, gauze, and other unmentionables. No coolie would consent to cleaning out the manholes, and I could not order nurses to do things like that. Therefore I cleaned out the manholes myself, much to the distress of our two senior nurses, who insisted upon helping me, getting themselves just as dirty as I.

All this was completely beyond Ai Sai's experience. But he watched us repeatedly at our thankless task until he began to get the idea. Then he took over. Now he understands these things better than I do, reports to me when major repairs are necessary, and tells me just how those repairs should be carried out. And I always obey his orders.

He was separated from me by the Japanese drive, which cut us off from Namkham in 1942. By then Dr. Ai Lun's wife, E Hla, had become Number Two in the hospital in his eyes, and he stayed with them in Lashio throughout the Japanese occupation. When Ai Lun left to finish his medical education in Lucknow and E Hla returned to our staff, Ai Sai returned also and re-attached himself to me. All of his postal savings were lost as a result of the war. Somewhat provoked, he began saving again and is now rather well-to-do for a Shan. You would never guess it from his clothes. I have given him clothes; I have ordered him to buy new clothes and wear them. But he won't wear them. Since it is his own choice to do all the dirty jobs that no one else will consent to undertake, he dresses the part. He keeps his clothes clean, but both shirt and baggy Shan pants are always torn and frayed, the rents in his trousers pinned together with nails, rusty safety pins or odd pieces of bamboo.

During these years Ai Sai has become fluent in Burmese. He learned, long since, the differences between a good nurse and bad one. When a nurse—even a staff nurse—makes an inexcusable mistake or tries to goldbrick, he uses his excellent Burmese and flays her alive. And she takes it!

During our great days, before the insurrection, we had so many stores that we had to convert the half-wrecked bungalow just behind the nurses' home into a storehouse. Since anybody could have broken in easily, Emily asked Ai Sai to give up his hut near my house, his special pride and joy, and live in a room in the storehouse. There Ai Sai kept his strong box, with all his treasure, chained to his bed.

Since Communism took over China there has been an exodus of Shans from China, with resultant rapid growth of villages on the Burma side of the line. A few of these refugees who had criminal tendencies settled in a village a mile east. Two of these gentlemen learned of Ai Sai's wealth and cased the joint until they knew all of his habits. One day just at dawn, the leader posted himself outside. Then his accomplice entered Ai Sai's room with a stolen rifle and demanded the keys to the chain and box. Although half-asleep, Ai Sai knocked the muzzle of the gun up, yelled for help, and he and the would-be robber began a struggle which resulted in their rolling out of the house, across the verandah, and down the steps to the courtyard behind the nurses' home.

By this time every nurse was awake and screaming, and a task force of Kachin, Shan, and Karen girls was scrambling to Ai Sai's assistance, while another group was running for Dr. Ai Lun and still a third the much longer distance to my house. Before the first group could grapple with the robber the gun exploded harmlessly and the robber ran off. Had he not done so, the nurses would undoubtedly have torn him to pieces.

I am not the only person who loves Ai Sai.

Late February, 1954, came. It was early on a cold Sunday evening, but my hospital consultations had been light, and I was sitting sprawled in front of my fireplace trying to get warm and trying still harder to find the words and phrases that might convince Americans that Burma is a country well worthy of her respect and affection. Somebody banged on the back door.

"Why don't you come in? The door is open," I shouted in Burmese, thinking it was a nurse coming to call me for an emergency.

The visitor walked in through the kitchen and dining room and I looked over the rims of my reading glasses at a man draped from neck to hips with more varieties of cameras than I had thought were for sale in all the world's markets.

"An American!" I said, starting to my feet. "God bless you for coming! Did the Government really permit you to come here?"

"They did. I'm Pete Kalischer, and I came up to do an article on you for *Collier's* Magazine."

"And the Government knew you were going to do an article on Seagrave and still let you come here!" I marveled.

"That wasn't all they did," said Pete. "I came into Burma on a ten-day visa. The Shan State officials told me I'd never be able to visit you with only a ten-day limit, so I went to Union Government officials and they extended my visa to twenty days, just so I could have plenty of time with you. I was told the Burma Government has never before been known to extend a transit visa after the visitor reached the country. But they did it for me, when they knew where I was going."

Pete went over big among all our people. He started work

at once taking candid camera snaps and close-ups of our Sunday evening song service. I explained to the nurses and school boys and girls that American photographers didn't like their subjects to watch the birdie and asked them to ignore the crazy American, no matter how crazy he acted. There were wide grins and chuckles of appreciation, and the song service went on as if Pete wasn't in the room. As soon as he knew there was no criticism of any of his actions he stepped all over everybody—most distinctly not permissible in Burma except to a "crazy American"—and took snaps of everything, even during the prayer at the end of the service.

In town at the bazaar, in the hospital wards, in the nurses' home, everywhere, Pete was good for laughs and, laughing, some of our really seriously ill patients began to get well.

When Pete arrived in Namkham a group of Catholic Kayah soldiers mistook him for a priest and knelt and kissed his hand. By the time he left everyone felt like hugging him and kissing him on the cheek. He is an American ambassador without portfolio.

It was May, 1954, and I was going through a list of consultations in the hospital when an Assistant to the Shweli Amat, the Administrator for our valley, came into the room.

"Former President Sao Shwe Thaike, who is now the Honorable Speaker of the House of Nationalities, and his mahadevi, together with the American Ambassador and his wife, are arriving in Namkham tomorrow afternoon between two and four. Can you put them up?"

"Do you mean Ambassador Sebald himself is coming?"

"He's the man."

"Oh gosh! Then I am in trouble up to my ears again, I guess."

"No, you're not," smiled the official, comfortingly.

"Of course I'll put them up."

"Let us know if there's anything we can do to help."

I sent for the Louisville-trained girls, the only ones who know from experience how Americans like things, and asked them to organize a team of nurses to fix up the big bedroom for the former president and first lady and the smaller one for Ambassador and Mrs. Sebald and to put a cot for me into the dining room behind a screen.

Doctor Ai Lun promised to consult with the authorities and find out just how we might appropriately do honor to our very important guests. Schoolmistress Ella took charge of preparing festal leis and bouquets for the nurses to bestow at the right time, and the two matrons took steps immediately to see that the hospitals, the nurses' home, and the nurses were as presentable as possible.

Next morning Ai Lun came back from town, saying he had been given special permission by the authorities to fly the flag of the Union of Burma from the hospital flagstaff in honor of the former president and also to fly my American flag from a separate flagstaff below the Union flag and in the correct position with respect to the Union flag required by protocol.

I took my flag out of my trunk and promptly began to worry again. The hospital's Union flag had been obtained in the days when flags of the best material were not obtainable. It was of light, flimsy cloth. My American flag was of superb material, heavy, and, of all things, larger than the Union flag. But permission had been granted, and the flags were flown according to protocol.

Our guests could only stay the night, so we had to give up the big official banquet we had hoped to have at Ai Lun's house next day. There was only time for a rapid tour of the hospital. The ex-president and his mahadevi were greatly impressed with the Burmese woman who had been in the hospital for a year after a Chinese Nationalist bullet destroyed one knee and the other hip while I did an arthroplasty on the hip. They promised to get in touch with her family in lower Burma and let them know where she was. Mrs. Sebald's heart was touched by another Burmese lady who had been ill twenty years and had finally sold her earrings so she could pay for the trip to Namkham from Communist-infested country two hundred and fifty miles southwest. Mrs. Sebald made a gift to the patient to permit her to redeem her earrings. When I explained about the gift the patient turned to me in absolutely typical Burmese fashion.

"Thank God!" she said. "I have been worried because I had no money left to show my appreciation for your treatment of me. Now I have something. I can stop worrying and begin to get well."

After the tour Sao Shwe Thaike and the ladies went off to do the town while the Ambassador excused himself to browse around with his camera before returning to chat with me to my infinite comfort.

That evening we had dinner around the great table on my screened porch—just the senior staff members and the guests.

"Sir," I said to Sao Shwe Thaike: "We have been friends so long that I must apologize. I find it hard to refer to you as 'Your Honor' or 'Your Excellency' or 'The Honorable Speaker.' I keep thinking of you as my friend still, in spite of my trial for treason and my jail sentence. I trust I am not impertinent."

"Old Man," replied that dignified gentleman—I love him when he calls me that—"when you were in jail and I was president I wanted with all my heart to visit you, but it was against the law."

"It would not have done, Sir," I answered. "But before you knew that suspicion had ceased and that permission was being granted for my return to Namkham you paid me a great compliment. You sent me a formal invitation to a great dinner at the president's house. I did not receive the invitation until I was back in Namkham, so I could not accept it. I could not have gone anyway because I didn't have my dinner coat in Rangoon. But your invitation restored a great deal of my self-respect and gave me strength to rebuild our hospital work to the state in which you now see it."

Before they left Ambassador Sebald told me he had been taking pictures of the Stars and Stripes flying so bravely under the flag of the Union of Burma, with Communist China just an air-mile away in the background. To him it was the symbol of the way this hospital works for Burma: Americans and Burmese working side by side in faith in the future of a great country, menaced though it be on all sides.

To me there were some details about those two flags which made the picture even better. The Burma flag was above the American flag as it should and must always be in Burma. The Burman should come first in everything. While our guests were here the breeze was just enough to move the heavy folds of the Stars and Stripes so everyone could see its beauty. But it was strong enough so the flag of Burma waved completely unfurled, with its own beauty dominating the scene, beauty made more beautiful still by the quiet Stars and Stripes below it.

America, rich, skilled, quietly and effectively giving support and help to Burma. Burma going ahead on its own, learning its lessons through adversity, eventually attaining its own well-deserved influence, not only in Burma but in the world. America can still teach Burma much. It will not be long until Burma can teach America some lessons. A start has already been made.

Five hours ago, as I was leaving the hospital, I met again the Colonel of the Chin Battalion which has just taken over our Frontier.

"I'll be seeing you again, Colonel," I said. "Our work will be dovetailing together from now on."

"Doctor, we are with you!" said the Colonel.